A SPECIAL NOTE ABOUT THIS BOOK

The Views of Dr. René Dubos, Professor of Environmental Biomedicine at The Rockefeller University

Many readers of *Peril on the Job* will probably find the book frightening. But I found it reasonable and constructive.

The facts reported by Ray Davidson are indeed frightening; if they did not frighten me it is simply because I was aware of most of them. Indeed, I suspect that the problems of industrial disease will probably soon become even more alarming than appears from what Mr. Davidson reports and postulates. It is fairly easy to estimate the numbers of workers killed or made obviously sick by industrial poisons. But this is only one part of the story. Levels of toxic materials so low that they do not cause obvious health disturbances exert in many cases deleterious effects that become detectable only long after initial exposure—often after many years. This is well recognized with regard to ionizing radiations and cigarette smoking. It is certainly true also for a host of substances widely used in industrial processes. Many chronic and degenerative diseases that now plague our society—the so-called diseases of civilization —can probably be traced to increase in the prevalence of chemical pollutants. From this point of view, it is surprising and indeed disturbing that the campaign for a better environment has placed so little emphasis on the fact that a large percentage of industrial plants—as well as offices —expose workers to highly objectionable environmental conditions—not only unpleasant, but potentially dangerous. All over the world, millions upon millions of workers are the guinea pigs of the technological environment.

I found *Peril on the Job* a reasonable book because it acknowledges the social complexities of the problems posed by health protection in industrial plants. Concern for efficiency and the economy must of course prevail at all levels of management; this is true irrespective of political system—capitalist, socialist, or communist. As stated by Mr. Davidson, "Most managers assert that they are deeply concerned with the health and safety of their employees. Most of them are undoubtedly sincere. But for a manager to take really effective action to protect his employees puts him squarely into conflict with his basic role in the profit system"—and indeed in any social system.

When a decision has to be made between safety and production, safety is in almost all cases the loser. This is not because of criminal neglect, as Mr. Davidson acknowledges. "There probably is not a manager in North America who would knowingly cause or permit a death even to save a million dollars. But the financial incentives pressing on managers to take risks leading to possible illness, injury or death are overwhelming. Management spokesmen testifying before legislative bodies assert that they have financial incentives as well as humanitarian reasons for maintaining safe and healthful work places, but this is not quite true. By and large, it pays to operate equipment until it collapses rather than keep it in constantly good repair. To make repairs for health and safety sake is a nonproductive cost item."

In most cases, furthermore, the supervisor is incapable of making health judgments; he has been trained primarily to keep production going and is acquainted only with primitive safety measures. Finally, few are the situations where there is enough knowledge of health effects to permit adequate medical management. And this brings me to the constructive aspects of the book.

So little is known of industrial medicine that vast research programs are needed to determine the potential dangers of the various types of working conditions. Some of these programs must be focused of course on the development of medical techniques for the treatment of the disease after it has become manifest. But equally or perhaps more important is the search for causes of disease, since only this kind of knowledge can provide a basis for the formulation of preventive measures. In other words, the environment must be studied as much as the disease. Another requirement is to learn to incorporate environmental knowledge in the design of plants and processes. At present, "metallurgy and fluid dynamics get more attention than men . . . cryogenics are better researched than emphysema. . . . Precise design of the shipping drums will be specified, but nothing is said about the man to fill the drum or what the material in the drum will do to him." Clearly the time has come to give as much thought to working conditions and health hazards as is given to engineering design and to purchase specifications.

There are, furthermore, important psychological aspects to the formulation and application of safety rules. The worker does not like to be talked down to; he wants to be "taken into partnership in a manner which reveals no condescension by the other party." Effective application of safety rules calls for more than a simple enunciation. It requires explanation, discussion, and participation. This is particularly true with regard to health matters less obvious and more complex than traumatic accidents.

In my opinion, it is unrealistic to hope that safety measures could completely prevent industrial diseases, even if they were based on much greater knowledge than we now have. New procedures and substances are continuously being introduced into industrial operations, so rapidly that there is no chance to evaluate their potential dangers to health. The only way to deal with this unhappy but inevitable state of affairs is to carry out on samples of the working population a variety of simple clinical tests, to the end of detecting as early as possible any change in the state of health. This approach could be called prospective epidemiology or medical alarm system.

Maintaining adequate health policies and medical alarm systems will be costly. But the cost, however great, will be small compared with the medical load now created by the chronic disabilities resulting from industrial exposure—let alone humanitarian considerations. In a truly civilized society, protection of the worker should be regarded as the most essential, irreducible aspect of production cost. Technology is constantly creating new environments, but modern men still have the anatomical and physiological needs and limitations our caveman ancestors had. We have no instinct to warn us of dangers that lurk in a new kind of vapor or in an invisible beam of radiation. The worker cannot possibly take responsibility for his health in a complex world which he does not control and which the experts themselves do not fully understand. Technological societies can survive and remain successful only if they learn to take into account in the price system the protection of the labor force engaged in the production of economic wealth, as well as the environment in which they live.

The problems posed by *Peril on the Job* are not peculiar to the chemical industries; they apply to all aspects of technological civilization. We shall experience human and ecological disasters unless we learn to give as much attention to man and the environment as we do to the production of goods. This requirement need not interfere with the efficiency of the technological enterprise and the maintenance of high living standards. Anyone familiar with the history of science and technology knows that progress has always resulted from the necessity to meet reasonable constraints and regulations. Scientists and technologists are so inventive that they can and will improve technological efficiency even as they develop working conditions compatible with the maintenance of health.

PERIL ON THE JOB

A Study of Hazards in the Chemical Industries

By RAY DAVIDSON

Public Affairs Press, Washington, D. C.

TO ALL THOSE MEN AND WOMEN WHO EARN
THEIR BREAD BY WORKING FOR WAGES

Published by Public Affairs Press
419 New Jersey Ave., S.E., Washington, D.C. 20003
Copyright, 1970, by Ray Davidson
Printed in the United States of America
Library of Congress Catalog Card No. 72-137830

Foreword

From its inception, the Oil, Chemical & Atomic Workers International Union (AFL-CIO) has had a deep sense of concern about the health and safety conditions prevailing in the plants where its members work, as well as a more general interest in improving working conditions throughout industry as a whole.

This interest—and indeed growing anxiety—has been rapidly developing in the union under the administration of President A. F. Grospiron. Like a number of other trade union leaders who have become concerned with the problems of industrial safety and health, Grospiron soon came to the conclusion that very little is being done to protect the safety of some 80 million Americans during their hours at the workplace—and even less concern is manifested for the protection of their health while on the job. Furthermore, not nearly enough basic information about this subject is available.

To develop a necessary bank of information, President Grospiron suggested to the various staff people employed by the Oil, Chemical & Atomic Workers that they pursue the subject, each in his own way. These activities have been carried on under the provisions of a policy resolution adopted by the union's convention in 1967. It is a program that has won wide support and cooperation from all elements in the organization.

Particular initiative in the pursuit of this assignment was shown by the union's "man in Washington", Anthony Mazzocchi, who bears the title of Citizenship-Legislative Director. As he tried to assemble health and safety testimony for presentation to Congressional committees, Mazzocchi discerned that workmen could tell the story better than many of the so-called experts. Accordingly, he brought men from industrial plants into Washington to testify before Congressmen and Senators.

To broaden the opportunities for workmen to tell their stories, the Oil, Chemical & Atomic Workers launched a series of regional meetings in which men and women from the plants could describe their problems and discuss them with scientists who volunteered their time and expertise. Most notable among these volunteer scientists has been Glenn Paulson of the Department of Environmental Biomedicine of The Rockefeller University, New York.

This book grew out of the descriptions of plant working conditions presented by various members of OCAW at those regional meetings. President Grospiron and the author concluded that the stories these men had to tell deserved a far wider audience and more detailed attention. As a result, the president of the union requested the author to gather additional data; in the months that followed, visits were paid to a number of chemical and petrochemical centers throughout the United States and Canada, and in-depth interviews were conducted with several hundred union members.

This report is essentially the story told by those workers to the author; it was supplemented with a modest amount of research to provide needed background information. Of the hundreds of volumes which have been written about labor, there probably is not one which is so truly a story told by the rank-and-file-workers, as contrasted to stories told by union leaders or outside observers.

Names are used—names of the men who describe working conditions and names of the particular companies and particular plants on which they report. A relatively small number of plants from the vast industrial complex are cited. There is no intention to single out these particular companies for special criticism: the conditions described are widespread throughout industry.

This report is critical of industrial management; the criticism is aimed *not at individual managers*, but at *the system of management* as it affects the health and safety of working people.

Corporate managers of good will should welcome this report as an instrument offering modest suggestions for the correction of flaws in the system—or, more accurately, how they can *participate in partnership with others* in correcting the system. As for the blame: where the shoe does not fit it need not be worn.

Grateful thanks must be extended to many. First, appreciation must go to A. F. Grospiron, a union leader with unusual qualities of concern, innovation and stubborn dedication. His concern with the environment of all people in the world and his specific actions in expressing that concern have made Oil, Chemical & Atomic Workers the foremost of all labor unions in environmental activities.

Thanks go to hundreds of members and to staff employees of the union who helped. Special acknowledgment must be extended to Anthony Mazzocchi for his initiative in seeking and collecting first-hand reports of health and safety problems at regional meetings of the union. Technical help by Glenn Paulson is appreciated. Frederick A. Linde, special assistant to President Grospiron for health and safety matters, has made an invaluable contribution, as a licensed professional chemical engineer and as a former chemical plant manager, by checking the manuscript for technical accuracy and by suggesting many pertinent additions and clarifications.

Personal thanks must go to two work associates—Jerry Archuleta, who took over the author's regular work so that he could assume responsibility for this volume, and to Jean Nickolas, who worried with each comma, each semi-colon, each fact that needed re-verification, with painstaking care and loyalty.

RAY DAVIDSON

Denver, Colorado

Contents

1

Speak of Life, Not of Numbers

The records say that somewhat over 14,000 men and women are killed and 2.2 million are injured seriously enough to lose time from work in the United States each year as they labor to earn their daily wages, but the records are tragically incomplete.

Counted in the statistics are only those who die violently and some, not all, of those who are injured by physical accidents such as fires, or falls from high places. Not counted are thousands more who die at home or in hospitals because of health damage suffered in their places of work. Not counted are still others who are prematurely aged, or suffer crippled bodies or minds from insidious, hard-to-pinpoint health hazards they were exposed to while earning their bread.

Therefore it is essential to disregard presently available statistics when considering the hazards of modern industrial work. The available data is demonstrably incomplete. Besides, even if the figures were accurately tabulated, they would miss the point. Death does not come in increments of hundreds or thousands, but to one person at a time. The breath stops, the heart stops, the quickening of the flesh ceases. The impact is felt only by a few intimates. A widow weeps.

It is pointless to say that more people die in automobile wrecks than in industrial accidents; one premature death from either cause is one too many. Actually, industrial work probably causes more deaths than automobiles. The complete facts are not in. Some work casualties are counted as such, some are not. When a man falls from a scaffold and dies while at work, he becomes a statistic in the industrial death record. But what of other deaths due to illness or premature aging caused by exposure to one or more of the innumerable toxic materials handled daily by hundreds of thousands of workmen? Even closest intimates usually fail to detect the imperceptible approach of death in this form. Even the victim is unsure what it is that slows his pace.

When death comes, the doctor's certificate may cite "pneumonia" or "heart stoppage," but the real cause may be fumes or dust inhaled at work over the months and years.

More tragic than the deaths, perhaps, are the cases of men who become old at a time when they should be in the prime of life. This burden weighs most heavily on workers who find themselves slowing up and losing confidence in themselves as men and breadwinners. Numbers in neat columns do not reflect such industrial casualties, grievous as they are.

When young Jimmy Owen died of carbon monoxide asphyxiation in the National Lead Company* plant at Sayreville, New Jersey, he represented, statistically, just a minute adjustment in that infinite combination of numbers which can be formed by varying the arrangement of the ten digits —1234567890. To his pregnant wife, Jimmy was, of course, the most important statistic in all creation.

Thurman Wooten is a casualty who does not turn up in the columns of numbers. At age 53 he is incapacitated by lung damage caused by breathing sulfuric acid fumes in the Farmers Chemical Company plant at Joplin, Missouri. He struggled for a while to support his family through part-time or light jobs; now he is hospitalized. Probably it cannot be proven that he is an industrial casualty, but he thinks so, his doctor thinks so, and if you talk with him you will think so, too. Your memory will be haunted by his face, a man too old at 53.

---

* Cases will be cited in this book from a number of specifically named plants. This is not to indicate, necessarily, that the companies named are any more or less reckless in health and safety matters than companies which are not named. The citations are random, intended to show conditions which are widely prevalent.

Benny Burrelle is 52 and looks younger. For many months he has been restlessly watching television, taking pills and whiling away the hours in his modest but tidy home near Picayune, Mississippi. Burrelle walks in a vaguely unnatural way—there is partial paralysis of his lower legs.

Brown-McCarthy Clinic and Tulane University physicians in New Orleans provide this medical diagnosis in Burrelle's case: "Acrylamide toxicity with neuropathy and dermatitis, hypertensive vascular disease, hypometabolism, mild polycythemia." He was poisoned by acrylamide, a chemical used in paper manufacture, while at work in the American Cyanamid Company plant near New Orleans. He may or may not be a digit in the statistics. After some delay, the company finally recognized his case as qualifying for workmen's compensation. This, plus an insurance policy, provided Burrelle with $74 a week for a few months.

But even several months after Benny Burrelle went off work because of acrylamide poisoning, American Cyanamid was boasting, on a large sign near the plant gate, "255 Days Without a Lost-Time Accident." Is Burrelle a statistic?

One by one, men like these—and their families—suffer. A nation hell-bent to achieve a Gross National Product of one trillion dollars annually just does not see or hear these people. As Ralph Nader told Senator Ralph Yarborough in a Senate Committee hearing in 1968:

"I think the problem of industrial safety has not been glamorous enough for the kind of reporting which perhaps has been directed toward plane crashes or submarine disasters, for example. These are men and women who are dying silently or who are being injured silently."

Death and health impairment in the work place are not glamorous to describe. The story is at best dull and at worst ugly. It is a story of strange, delayed reactions to esoteric chemicals such as phosgene gas. It is a story of men choking and coughing day after day from exposure to chlorine gas, of men working hour after hour in dust so thick they cannot see beyond

20 feet, of men wading in acid solutions. It is a story of mis-
management of American industry, for upon management rests
most of the responsibility for the occupational illnesses and
deaths.

The blame which falls on management is collective rather
than individual. In only rare cases can a particular foreman,
supervisor, plant manager or corporate president be held specifically accountable for a death or injury or a case of work-
caused emphysema or cancer. Nearly all of the abuses to human
health come from overall attitudes, methods, practices and approaches followed by the managerial system. The root causes
are complex as our industrial system is complex.

This book is an attempt to identify those root causes and
the system of management which is responsible for the casualties. It is an attempt to portray industrial health and safety
conditions as they actually exist. The matter has been approached from its underside, from the human side where the
suffering occurs, rather than from the over-view of theory or
broad statistics. In this approach, the author has engaged in
detailed interviews with hundreds of workers employed in
chemical, oil and related industries.

Who can better tell the story than the men who breathe the
toxic fumes, inhale the irritating dusts, absorb through their
skins the poisonous liquids and otherwise take risks and endure
hazards in order to earn their daily bread?

Although the workers quoted in this book are employed
chiefly in chemical and related industries, there is every indication that similar health hazards exist in other industries and
even in many non-industrial places of employment. Hazardous
materials are used in all industries. They are found in the
chrome on your car, in the cosmetics used by women and in the
bread sold in your super-market.

A survey conducted in 1968 under the sponsorship of the
Chicago Institute of Medicine examined occupational health
exposures in 803 representative work places employing 260,000
people in the Chicago metropolitan area. The establishments

studied included not only manufacturing plants, but also transportation, wholesale and retail trade, and services such as hotels and places of entertainment. By projection, these 803 job sites are representative of 14,453 such, employing 1,048,398 in the area. This survey showed that in 73 percent of the work places there was exposure to one or more potentially health-hazardous materials, such as toxic solids, liquids or gases.

A similar finding was reported by Dr. William H. Stewart, Surgeon General of the United States. In 1968, he told a Congressional Committee that studies by the Public Health Service revealed 65 percent of industrial workers to be exposed to toxic materials or harmful physical agents such as severe noise or vibration. His investigators examined controls that were supposed to protect the workers from toxic agents and found that only 25 percent of the workers were adequately safeguarded. "The remaining workers were plainly unprotected or working in conditions which needed immediate attention," Dr. Stewart said.

In this more specific report of health hazards in chemical and related industries, certain general points will be made by the stories the workers tell:

• Management operates by the dollar yardstick; all other measurements are secondary. Because dollar value cannot be put on human life and health, even the best-intentioned managers are handicapped and frustrated. Life and health are intangibles which cannot be entered on ledger sheets or production reports.

• Closely related is excessive zeal for production—a zeal that has made America the greatest of the industrial nations. Production has become a way of industrial life that is almost obsessive. Like race drivers on the track, some managers become almost completely preoccupied with the slogan, "Faster! Faster!"

• Science is worshipped like a god in America. Yet science, supposedly precise and factual, is full of unknowns. Industrial workers, and most of their supervisors, blindly grope through a chemical jungle full of lurking dangers they do not know and cannot identify.

• In an indirect but very real sense, the greatest killer of all is, perhaps, bureaucracy. Corporate managers speak of responsibility as a first article of faith, but in most companies responsibility is so diffused that it cannot be accurately attributed to any one executive. The left hand may dispense healing balm while the right hand is committing manslaughter and the higher authority at the head is out of contact with both. Or, to use a different analogy, all too many corporate machines run as if they had lives and wills of their own, like robots out of human control.

The result is an extraordinary amount of disorder. And there is practically no law at all to govern the situation; although America is hailed as a nation of laws, there is little effective law reaching into industrial facilities. Behind their walls and chain-link fences, our factories operate as independent fiefdoms responsible in no large measure to any sovereign.

2

The Chemical Jungle

One summer day in 1968, W. A. Moore and B. J. Puckett were assigned to clean out the paranitroaniline dryer in the Shreveport, Louisiana, plant of Universal Oil Products Company. They finished the job, showered, changed clothes and left the plant in late afternoon.

As Moore approached the front door of his home, he keeled over. His wife called an ambulance and took him to Willis Knight Hospital. An emergency room doctor was momentarily confused as to the relationship of Moore and Mrs. Moore because Moore, normally white-skinned, had turned black as a result of paranitroaniline poisoning.

While Moore was receiving treatment, an automobile drew up bearing Puckett. He, too, had collapsed from paranitroaniline damage to the blood. F. Q. Hood, secretary of the local union which represents the employees of the plant, tells the story. "It seems that Puckett had gone to his uncle's fishing camp on nearby Lake Caddo for an outing. There, he told his relatives he was just too tired to eat and that he wanted to lie down," Hood recalls. "It seems that just before Puckett laid down he told his relatives, 'You know, I've been working in some chemicals and they tell me that if I get sick I should go to Willis Knight Hospital.' Right after that he passed out."

A member of the family drove Puckett thirty miles to the hospital. Fortunately, this particular hospital had staff doctors who happened to be familiar with the effects of paranitroaniline. The lives of Puckett and Moore were saved. The evidence is that the two men absorbed the chemical, in dust form, through their unbroken skins. Apparently the hot summer weather was a factor, opening their pores and increasing absorption. Paranitroaniline converts the blood's oxygen-carrying hemoglobin into methemoglobin, which cannot effectively carry oxygen to the body tissues. Milder degrees of exposure often results in what is called "blue lip"—a bluing of lips and the flesh under fingernails.

Compounds made from paranitroaniline, an "organic intermediate" in the chemists' jargon, are used in many products. One is as a corrosion inhibitor in gasoline. Another is in red lipstick.

John Kennedy, an employee of the Great Lakes Chemical Company at El Dorado, Arkansas, works in the manufacture of Tetrabrome, a fire retardant for fabrics. As in the case of many other chemicals, Tetrabrome affects people differently. Kennedy himself has never discerned any ill effects from exposure to it. "But," says Kennedy, "I have gone on shift and the men I would be relieving would be in such condition that they couldn't see or tell who you were until you got up close to them. I'm talking particularly about Coy Lowery and Wayne Hall. I've had to hold Coy up by his belt buckle, hold him up while he could weld. He just couldn't stand up."

Other symptoms felt by workers exposed to this product are dizziness, lack of balance, numbness in legs, and weakened sexual functions.

A. G. Rainwater of the same plant finally took his problem to the Scott-White Clinic in Temple, Texas, a regionally prestigious institution. "I was never sick most of my life," as Rainwater tells it, "but after going to work for Great Lakes I've been in the hospital three times. They kept telling me I just had the 'nerves.' I couldn't lay it on anything, but I kept getting the jitters and circulation troubles. I'd get cold and my arms and legs would go dead. They'd be cold, I couldn't get much life in them. They'd take me to the hospital and I'd lie there three, four or five days and get all right and come on back to work again. Kind of a peculiar thing to have."

Rainwater's work exposed him to bromine, methylbromide, ethyl bromide and methanol. Doctors at Scott-White said Rainwater was suffering from bromism resulting from an overdose of bromine or one of its derivatives or compounds. This, he was told, could make a person nervous or it could act as a sedative, but that an extreme overdose "affects your nerves no end."

Chronic poisoning by methylbromide injures the central nervous system. Lung, liver and kidneys also may be damaged. Methanol, commonly known as wood alcohol, is a narcotic, toxic to the central nervous system and the optic nerves. Rainwater and others in the Great Lakes plant are exposed regularly to all these materials. Who knows what the combined effects of these may be on their long-term health?

Carlo Lovi was overcome by chlorine gas in the National Lead Company plant at Sayreville, New Jersey, on March 22, 1969. He went to the plant's first aid room and was given penicillin shots for three consecutive days, plus a cough syrup. Again on April 16 and still again on May 3 he inhaled a combination of gases. Fellow workers testify to Lovi's discomfort, his persistent choking and coughing. On May 4 he vomited on the street en route home from work. Upon entering his home that evening, he told his wife he felt he was dying, said he loved his family and fell on his bed unconscious. Mrs. Lovi sent him to a hospital; during and after hospital treatment he was off work for several weeks.

Chlorine is perhaps the most commonly used of all industrial gases. Tens of thousands of workmen are exposed to it daily, often in concentrations far above safe limits. Older people recall chlorine as a World War I chemical warfare gas. World War II soldiers were spared from chemical warfare, but most ex-GIs were given precautionary training in gas identification, being taught to detect the principal gases by smell. Almost all remember the peculiar phosgene odor, a quite pleasant smell like that of new-mown hay.

Phosgene, a component in many synthetics, is a common industrial chemical in America today. It is moved about the country in tanker trucks and railroad tank cars. In 1969, phosgene killed Chris Anderson in the Ott Chemical Plant in Muskegon, Michigan. Due to poorly compensated hydrostatic pressure, a seal flew off a vaporizer and hot liquid phosgene sprayed over Anderson's chest.

Insidiously, phosgene has a delayed reaction; usually two to 24 hours pass before the victim suffers. Anderson came out of the polluted area and sat down in the plant lunchroom for a couple of hours. He breathed emergency oxygen for a while, said he felt better and wanted to go back to work. The doggedness with which most skilled workmen stick to their jobs defies explanation. Anderson went back out into the plant, but 20 minutes later he collapsed and four hours after that he died in a Muskegon hospital.

Cautious workmen—and cautious managers—believe that a man exposed to phosgene should go immediately to a hospital intensive care unit for close observation. Since Anderson's death, the management at Ott has let it be known that any man who undergoes phosgene exposure is free to leave work and get to a hospital, but management does not insist that the men do so.

Bill Parmelee, president of the local union in the Ott plant, comments on the exposure in the plant thus: "In the time I've worked there (five years), I've had two or three accidents with phosgene and some accidents with carbamate and acid chlorides. Every man who has worked there has asked himself, some time or other, 'Okay, I had an accident with phosgene—I got away with it. I had an accident with this—I've gotten away with it. How long is it going to be before I have some effects from these? Each one, taken in itself, wouldn't seem like too much, but over a period of years, if this is going to be my life's work, how long will it be before I'm one of the guys on the list?' "

The dangers of the chemical jungle sometimes are taken into the homes of the workers. Consider the experience of Jim Breaux, who works in the same American Cyanamid plant as Benny Burrelle, near New Orleans. While at work, Breaux accidentally was sprayed with a small amount of acrylonitrile (akin to acrylamide) as he drew a small sample of the material from a processing unit. Some of the chemical dried on his shirt. Shortly after Breaux got home from work, he accompanied his wife to the supermarket, carrying their 13-month-old daughter in his arms while Mrs. Breaux pushed the grocery cart. Apparently the infant's nose was pressed close to the spot of dried acrylonitrile on Breaux's shirt. Suddenly the child experienced convulsions. "She went under about four o'clock and she didn't come out of it until about eight o'clock that evening," Breaux recalls.

The physician who treated the infant said at that time he did not know what caused the convulsions, but a few years later he said, "I'm pretty sure it was that acrylonitrile."

Medical advice about systemic injuries suffered in the chemical jungle tends to be confusing and vague. Most otherwise well-qualified physicians do not know much about industrial chemicals. Some fear to commit themselves because they do not want to become involved as witnesses in lawsuits. Some company doctors, like attorneys, seem to think that their sole responsibility is to protect, first and foremost, the clients who pay the fees—i.e., the companies.

A recitation of the deadly chemicals used in industry today has the sound of a Satanic litany. There is hydrogen cyanide, also called hydrocyanic acid or prussic acid. Minute amounts are used for executions in prison gas chambers; large amounts are used in industry. It is a component of acrylates and other plastics. Hydrogen sulfide, frequently found where oil is refined or natural gas is produced, is a gas highly toxic in both short term and long term respects. There is ammonia, used in many chemical processes. And in the manufacture of today's deadly insecticides of questionable environmental virtue, men are exposed daily to chemicals with such jawbreaking names as hexachlorocyclopentadiene.

The Olin Corporation plant at Ashtabula, Ohio, is a small facility. Its 45 non-supervisory employees handle 27 known deadly chemicals such as phosgene, chlorine, toluenediamine, tolylene diisocyanate and carbon monoxide. Jim Dioneff, union chairman and six-year employee in the facility, says, "We've had quite a few upsets where we've put phosgene and tolylene diisocyanate out into the air in great quantities and where we have knocked down at least 40 men at a time, not only in our place but also in adjoining plants." There is a strain in Dioneff's voice when he adds, "Lately, it hasn't been too bad. But we were sending a couple of men, say three or four times a year at least, to the hospital."

Of course not all the chemical hazards are so esoteric or so new. Men continue to suffer lead poisoning, a common ailment in the time of Julius Caesar; the nobility got it then because they made the mistake of using leaden utensils common people could not afford.

In recent Congressional testimony, Dr. Irving J. Selikoff of the Mount Sinai School of Medicine, City University of New York, noted that there "was this famous instance of the Schneeberg Mines of Saxony, where in 1879 cases of fatal lung tumors were reported among the workmen in this mine and to this day we still have workmen in the same mine dying of lung cancer." Uranium miners in Colorado, Utah and New Mexico are dying today, too, of lung cancer.

Asbestos is an old and comparatively well-researched industrial material; workmen who breathe in its particles continue to die. Indeed, so much of this cancer-causing material fogs into the air from construction projects that half of 3,000 consecutive autopsies performed in New York City showed at least some asbestos fibers in the bodies examined. Similar findings have been made in Pittsburgh, Miami and other cities. Yet it is mechanically feasible to prevent the spread of asbestos fibers into the air.

Old and new dangers lurk in the industrial jungle; the new proliferate year in and year out. No one knows how many different chemicals and industrial materials are now in use. The figure 450,000 is tossed around. "Protecting the Health of 80

Million Americans," a special report issued in 1966 by the U.S. Surgeon General, states, "It has been estimated that every 20 minutes a new, and potentially toxic, chemical is being introduced into industry. New processes and new sources of energy present occupational health problems of unprecedented complexity." The report adds that while automation makes possible the removal of some workers from hazardous environments, it also "can introduce unexpected or bizarre physical hazards."

A trivial example of the massive numbers of materials being handled is found in the sales catalog of the J. T. Baker Company of Phillipsburg, New Jersey. This is a small company, with only 311 non-supervisory workers, but its catalog offers for sale nearly 6,000 different chemicals. Such playing with numbers can go on forever; the author engages in it only to illustrate the confusion, not to suggest answers.

Industrial hygienists consider the most comprehensive reference book on the subject of chemical exposure hazards to be an impressive volume entitled, "Dangerous Properties of Industrial Materials," by Dr. N. Irving Sax. The third edition, 1968, of this tome lists more than 12,000 commonly used industrial materials, from acetoacet-*m*-xylidide to zoaline and including the juniper juice that flavors gin. Pertinently, the 1968 edition listing of 12,000 materials is an increase of 2,000 over the 1963 edition. Thus there has been introduced more than one new chemical per day, on average, on which Dr. Sax has been able to make hazard evaluations. There are many more on which even preliminary research apparently is unavailable. Some estimates indicate that 2,000 new materials are introduced into industrial processes annually.

The chemical jungle defies comprehension. Workmen and their managers stumble through it without adequate guidance. A person lost in a tropical jungle has at least a fairly reliable clue as to which berries are safe to eat: he watches the monkeys and eats what they eat. No such guidance is available in the chemical jungle. Even among the 12,000 materials identified by Dr. Sax, it is stated in the case of chemical after chemical that the toxicity is unknown. Particularly the chronic, or long-term, effects on the body are unknown.

Why are the toxicities unknown? Primarily because toxicological testing is laborious, highly specialized and very expensive. Management wants the very least time to elapse between paying for the initial research on a component or a product and marketing of the product. Testing stretches out the time interval; and, as a variable, testing is an option which is often waived. Thousands of chemicals, totally unlike any ever before encountered by man or the animals, are common items in the market place. Some effects—from cyanide, for example—are quick and certain. Others, such as cyclamate, are very slow and evidence can only be gathered by bits and pieces.

When the game is over and the score is added up, it is too late to repair the body or to correct the genetic mischief handed on to future generations. But since many chemicals are so different from those encountered in normal life, there are no guides, no lights in the forest. Each new item among the untold thousands is new and different unto itself and for each a new clearing must be made in the jungle.

The American Conference of Governmental Industrial Hygienists has established a Threshold Limit Value (TLV) on each of some 450 to 500 industrial materials. The Threshold Limit Value is the maximum exposure considered safe for an eight-hour work period, but industrial hygienists debate whether they are low enough. TLVs generally are neither comprehended by lower level production management nor appreciated by the workmen.

The TLVs usually are not enforced. Take chlorine, for example. The TLV for it is one part per million in air. The odor of chlorine is detectible at about 3.5 parts per million. If a man can smell it, it's already too late, because he's getting three and a half times more than he should over a sustained period.

John Aquaro, union safety chairman in the National Lead Company Sayreville plant, says that if there were an electronic chlorine monitoring device in the area of the plant where Carlo Lovi and many others have been chlorinated, and if that device were set at one part per million, "it would be ringing 90 percent of the time." Workmen in many other plants offer similar testimony of day-long exposure to chlorine strong enough to smell. Similar statements are made about many other known poisons.

The Manufacturing Chemists Association publishes what it calls a "Chemical Data Safety Sheet" on each of 90-odd of the more commonly used chemicals. Each of these goes into considerable detail about the health hazards of and the precautions to be followed in handling one chemical. They are well-written, quite readable by the person of average literacy—entirely practical. But they exist for only 90-odd chemicals and it is very rare that a company makes any of the data sheets available to industrial workers. To do this would raise annoying questions and well might interfere with the flow of production.

Many workers handle chemicals which are identified only by manufacturer's code numbers. The worker is instructed merely to "inject eight gallons of G-184 into each batch" of the product he is making.

"Is it dangerous?" the worker asks. Replies the foreman: "Well, just be careful; don't get any of it on you, and if you do, wash it off." (In most cases the foreman has not the slightest idea of the specific dangers posed.)

"Can you tell me the chemical content of G-184?" a worker may ask. "No, because it is an industrial secret" is a standard management reply.

Jack Stagner, union safety chairman in the Atlantic Richfield oil refinery in Houston, has tried to get the blindfolds removed from his fellow workers.

"Some years ago," he points out, "I got interested in the company's handling of chemicals of exotic nature because I've never been able to find out just what some of these chemicals were that I was asking about. Since that time, I have noticed that the company no longer displays chemicals as they prob-

ably would come from the manufacturer, where they have the
drum with the manufacturer's name on it, and the chemical's
trade name.

"Now, as I understand it, all the chemicals come through
Sand Springs, and as they come from there these barrels all
come in painted and all you see on them are the code names. A
code name will have a letter prefix with several numbers and
this tells us absolutely nothing.

"Meeting with the company, I've tried many a time to point
out the hazards. The management indicates, 'Well, look, if we
get some of these fellows working up there around the unit
and we tell them what this chemical actually is and what the
allied hazards are, well, they just wouldn't want to work there.'
This seems to be their attitude. They just don't want to tell
you what it is.

"So I have got the company to code the different chemicals
by a number classification—classification 1, 2, 3 or 4, number 4 being the most severe. They give you a chart. Incidentally, this chart is not displayed all over the plant. This is only
in areas where you ask for the darned thing and you have to
keep asking to get it. Number 4 would mean that it is hazardous
to breathe, and certainly you wouldn't want to get it on you
or swallow any of it, and this is about the extent of their explanation of what Class 4 chemical is. So we really don't know
what we are handling out there.

"I was talking to some people just the other night who work
in the labor department, working over the various parts of the
plant. These people never know what they are handling, not
even the products on the unit, let alone the chemicals in the
drums they are handling. This has been a tough row to hoe
and it seems like that rather than getting the company to take
some decisive action, all they've gone into is more evasion than
anything."

Question: Do you think a man is entitled to know the
exact chemical nature of what he is handling, plus all known

information as to the type of damage it could do—that is, whether it is a lung irritant or a nerve poison, or whatever?

Stagner: "He should certainly know the nature of the beast that it is."

The jungle is populated not only by big beasts but also by slithering serpents, ugly lizards, bugs, worms, stinging flies, leeches and all manner of little creatures which bite and sting, and by invisible germs and viruses which cause strange fevers, diarrhea, rashes and swellings.

The jungle is infested not only by lead, mercury, asbestos and all the old killers, but also by a proliferation of new poisons with unpronounceable names, and some of these are hidden behind meaningless trade names which say little, if anything, about the true contents and behind even more meaningless code numbers.

Protection against any one of the sickening agents is difficult enough; the problem of protection against several of them in combination scarcely has been given thought. Involved here is the synergistic effect. Synergistic means "working together" and it means that two and two do not necessarily equal four, but can equal five, ten or even 100. A homely example of the synergistic effect is found in the mixing of alcohol and barbiturates. A person may drink alcohol, go to bed and sleep soundly. He may take a barbiturate sleeping tablet and sleep soundly. But if he takes both alcohol and barbiturate, there is a serious danger of death.

Millions of workers in many industries are exposed to combinations of two, a half dozen, or a dozen different known toxic materials. It worries them. It must have worried the Surgeon General when he said, "The modern worker encounters health hazards which involve complex, often synergistic, interactions of numerous physical, chemical and even psychological agents." Ask the workers why they survive exposures and many of them look heavenward and reply, "The Man Upstairs must be looking after us."

Obviously, these dangers do not always compound. If they

did, there would be more deaths and illnesses. But the workers do not know where they stand as they inhale and touch the strange things. The scientific community, by splitting the atom, has unlocked the power that lights the stars. It has put men on the moon and brought them back again. But it has no comprehensive knowledge of the hazards of the mundane work place.

Chrome-plated and plastic-wrapped, we wander in an almost pathless wilderness.

3

In the Sweat of Thy Face

Working men accept the curse put on Adam: "In the sweat of thy face shalt thou eat bread." It is the way of life. Many men even enjoy physical derring-do. There's pride in hefting the heavy load, in swinging the 16-pound sledgehammer, in walking the high iron of construction. The sort of activity which causes clothing to soak with sweat on a hot summer day is taken as routine. But the new curses put on industrial workers represent something other than forthright challenges to manliness. Some are bizarre. "There hasn't been a man in the plant, unless he's been hired in the last few days, who hasn't had to go over to first aid for oxygen." That is the way union chairman Jim Dioneff describes the result of exposures to one or more of the 27 toxic gases in the Olin Chemical plant in Ashtabula, Ohio.

Some workaday curses are just plain damned miserable. "If you come into Department 11-IMP, you could look around and on the pipes and the beams the dust is anywhere from an eighth- to a half-inch thick," says Winfred Lawery, union committeeman, speaking of a department in the Monsanto plant at Trenton, Michigan, which processes insoluble metaphosphate. "The dust continuously flies while the operator is crushing this material into a powder form." Insoluble metaphosphate, a salt-like material, probably is no more dangerous to health than many other dusts people occasionally breathe, from time to time. But working in heavy concentrations of any kind of dust for long hours is, at best, unpleasant.

Monsanto employees also are annoyed by the dust from

sodium acid pyrophosphate, a material used in cake mixes. Workers exposed to the dust suffer severe nosebleeds. Ted Dominczyk was hospitalized with a nosebleed in 1968; the blood flow finally stopped the next day. According to Lawery, something curious happens after a person works around the sodium acid pyrophosphate for four or five months: he no longer has nosebleeds. The company management has decided that no man shall work in this cake-bake ingredient dust more than one day in every three. This provides one day for irritation, two days for healing. Some men in the department claim their sense of smell has been destroyed.

Adam Caban, local union vice president, estimates that 80 to 90 percent of the men employed in the soap department of the same Monsanto plant suffer skin rashes. A popular laundry detergent is made there but sold under the name of another firm—one of the larger soap companies.

Charles Candler, who works in the soap department, has a moderately persistent case of rash which has hung on for a year. Monsanto's doctor told Candler his rash was caused by something he ate. Company doctors are very prone to blame skin rashes on everything except the job. Strawberries (in and out of season), sunshine, milk chocolate and "not enough baths" are some of the well used "medical" explanations. They are easier and cheaper, certainly, than patch tests, medical detective work and skilled treatments. Candler went to a dermatologist who said, however, that the rash was caused by something he got on his skin.

Monsanto employees think the rashes have become more prevalent since the company started spraying dyes onto the soap to make the bright blue and green flecks which stand out in color television ads. Blue or green, it's still just plain detergent.

Because the dyes seem to bring difficulty, the union has asked Monsanto to reveal their chemical composition. The company refuses to do so on the ground that industrial spies might learn a trade secret. The problem in the plant perhaps would be solved by the elimination of color television from living rooms.

Ron Loupe, union chairman in the Vulcan Materials Company chemical plant near Baton Rouge, Louisiana, expresses dismay at the conditions there. The facility had been in operation a little more than a year in January, 1970, when Loupe said, "The acid section is about to fall to pieces." The result is spills of hydrochloric acid solutions. There is a sump into which the solution is supposed to drain, but often it overflows and a solution of 25 percent hydrochloric and 75 percent water covers the concrete floors. The men are provided with rubber shoes, which reach just above the ankle, when they are required to go wading in the solution.

"Sometimes I've seen the acid get right to the top of your boot," says Loupe. Asked if fumes rose from the solution, Loupe replies, "A bunch." And these fumes are among the most distasteful of all those found in industry. Hydrochloric acid is an unstable solution of hydrogen chloride and water. Even when it is cold, toxic and corrosive fumes evolve continuously. Concentrations of 35 parts per million cause irritation of the throat after short exposure, but the recommended Threshhold Limit Value for eight hours' exposure is only five parts per million.

There are two ways to erect a barrier between dusts, liquids or gases and the worker. The first, more efficient and more costly way is to use equipment which does not leak. The second way, less efficient and cheaper, is to shield the worker with gas mask, rubber coat and overalls, rubber boots.

Working in masks and rubber suits, even if safe, brings a rather extreme manifestation of the curse, "in the sweat of thy face." A few hours in a rubber suit, even in moderate temperatures, results in the concentration of much perspiration—there is no chance for the sweat to evaporate. Rubber gloves worn all day can contribute to skin troubles. The same, or worse, results may come from wearing rubber boots for long periods. Heavy rubber work gloves—cumbersome and thick compared to those women use in the kitchen—handicap the movements of a man who is handling tools, make him more clumsy and subject to accident.

Most industrial masks fit around the face just back of the nose and mouth. When blocked from entering the lungs, the dusts, and sometimes the vapors, concentrate even more heavily than otherwise on the sweaty skin at the edge of the mask and cause irritations and rashes.

Frustration with rubber suits, rubber gloves and masks sometimes drives men to take chances. Frank Farmer got a dangerous exposure to phenol in the Ott Chemical Company plant in Muskegon, Michigan, for this reason. According to Bill Parmelee, local union president, Farmer was trying to manipulate pipe wrenches with gloves on. The gloves and wrenches got slippery with phenol coming out of frozen lines he was repairing. "And so, being an old bull-of-the-woods maintenance man, he took off his gloves and tried to get at the job with his bare hands," Parmelee recalls. The phenol got on Farmer's hands and arms. After about two hours he came to the lunch room "pale as a ghost."

Farmer recovered after a few days in a hospital. Probably he was lucky; according to Sax, death has resulted from exposure of as little as 64 square inches of skin to phenol. What of Farmer's future? Phenol is a serious long-term toxic material, affecting the central nervous system, kidneys, liver and spleen.

Roger Lohman of the Ott plant reports that there are a "number of leaks of phenol through pumps and sample points and loose fittings. This phenol gets on the concrete or on the floor and lays right there, so it's forever present."

In the Vulcan Materials Company chemical plant at Baton Rouge, Louisiana, Robert Martin is frustrated by working with epichlorohydrin, a chemical used in the manufacture of lacquers and varnishes. Normally a light, water-like liquid, epichlorohydrin turns molasses-thick and sticky under certain conditions prevailing in the Vulcan plant. Workmen have to drain this material out into 55-gallon drums, and, because there are spills, they wear rubber boots and rubber gloves. Martin says, "We have masks but they've not been used too much. The stuff is so bad to work with, it's so heavy, it gets all over everything and every time you touch something it sticks. If you've got a mask on and you're trying to adjust it with your gloves on, you get it all up on your head and on your neck."

Martin has suffered severe rashes from epichlorohydrin. He asked Vulcan's laboratory technicians about the chemical but they seemed to know little about it. Sax gives it a high toxicity rating, both short and long term. Acute poisoning can cause respiratory paralysis; chronic poisoning causes kidney damage. Speaking about the spillage of epichlorohydrin, Martin says, "I imagine it's a half inch deep out there now, on the concrete."

For all-round messiness, two plants of the Humko Products Company in Memphis, Tennessee, stand out. This relatively small firm is a subsidiary of Kraftco, formerly known as National Dairies. One plant makes edible oil products such as margarine and salad oil from a variety of vegetable and animal fats. The other takes residues from this plant, along with additional animal and vegetable oils, and produces chemicals.

Coconut oil sounds innocuous enough, but men working around it suffer. "I get to the point where I can hardly breathe," says A. J. M. Shelton of the chemical plant. "This holds true with a majority of the men. You see them with red eyes, coughing and spitting and what have you, and trying to get just a decent breath." In the same plant, rape seed is spray processed into small, solid particles which, when combined with sweat, cause the men to break out in rashes.

John Thomas Minor, 42, died on November 10, 1969 while in a railroad tank car at Humko's edible oil plant. The car had contained palm oil and had been drained of the product. Minor was assigned to go inside the tank to save the oil left clinging to the inside by pushing out the sticky residue with a squeegee-like tool. Fumes overcame him and he died.

Less grave is the accident that occurred to Samuel Austin in the Stauffer Chemical Company plant at Chicago Heights,

Illinois. Says Austin, "I went down to the acid plant to put up some light bulbs. I came back and had to go over to the pipe shop. I was standing there talking to one of the pipefitters and I heard a hissing. I looked down at my shoes and they were on fire."

Austin had stepped in spilled phosphorous and water. After the water dried away, the phosphorous burst into flames because it is self-igniting in dry air. Austin stuck his feet in a sink and ran water over them to quench the fire. The shoes were not damaged too badly, but Austin was apprehensive about putting them in his locker for fear they would flare up again.

Francisco Montalvo, president of the local union, has a wry way of describing dust conditions in the same Stauffer plant: "We do have an integrated people out there. We have the colored people and we have the white people. But out of that di-calcium department, when they come out, everybody's white. Believe me, that dust is terrible!" James Cornwell, a fellow workers, adds: "This dust that he was talking about in di-calcium, it fogs completely out of the department. I drive a lift truck to the warehouse and there are times you go down through there and you can't even see a man if he walks out in front of you, it's so bad. There's nowhere for it to go. It just comes out there and settles down on the floor."

Robert Forrest, secretary of the local, describes the dust in the tri-sodium phosphate department. "Harold Green and I were working on the surge hopper, putting a level device on it. The dust was so bad we had dust respirators on, and goggles. We got the fumes so bad and our eyes got so bad that we almost couldn't see to get down off the scaffold. We had to go to first aid and get oxygen because the dust has so much chlorine in it. It's a very dusty hopper; no ventilation, hardly at all." Chlorinated tri-sodium phosphate is commonly added to household scouring powders to give them "bleach."

Carborundum Company's plant at Hickman, Kentucky, manufactures huge electrodes and anodes for use in steel mill electric furnaces. These are compounded of a mixture of graphite, iron oxide, powdered coke, and other solids, milled into a paste with oils. The paste is extruded into rods, some of them 14 to 16 inches in diameter and several feet long. These rods are packed in sand in a furnace, which essentially is just a large pit in the ground. There the rods are baked under high temperatures.

When the lid is taken off the furnace, the temperature is in the range of 600 degrees centigrade. Men must descend into the pit to scratch away the sand and attach hoisting lines for cranes to lift the electrodes or anodes out. Local union secretary J. T. Kennedy says of this work: "The only safety protection that these men have is that the company gives them wooden shoes. There have been cases where these shoes have caught fire when the man steps into the sand."

By the sweat of thy face!

The solid materials for these electrodes and anodes is ground into a fine, flour-like substance. Says Henry Callison, local union president: "You have these flour-like particles flying in the air at all times. It makes it bad on the men. When they come out of there in the evening, they have this black stuff all over them." Kennedy adds: "We have dust inside all of the buildings. The worst would be in the finishing department. They turn these electrodes down in lathes and they have grinders that take off part of the surface. You are in a closed building and that is really where it is worst of all. At times you can be at one end of the building and you can't see the man at the other end (about 100 feet away)."

It is a curious and persistent dust. Callison describes it this way: "For example, now, when you get off work—say Friday evening—you shower up, you don't work Saturday. Sunday you get up to go to church, you put on a white shirt. You've showered again Sunday morning before you go to church. Sunday when you come back at lunch from church you look at your collar at the neck, it is black. It works back up out of the pores of your skin."

An even more persistent discoloration of clothing is endured by some men in the Niagara Falls, New York, plant of the chemical division of Goodyear Tire and Rubber Company. "The people who are doing the bagging are the ones who are affected mostly by this," says Richard Credicott, union safety committee chairman. "It has a tendency to stain their clothes, T-shirts, shorts, or dress shirts. It discolors the collar. If you're working on the Nailex, it's orangish color."

Credicott, a soft-spoken man who voices only mild complaints, works in a relatively clean operations job. At the time he was interviewed on February 10, 1970, he had not worked in the department where he could get exposed to the Nailex dust for 10 days, yet yellow color was still seeping out of his pores and onto his clothing. He states that he doesn't know what chemical it is that oozes out of the skin. He has asked the management, but cannot get an answer. He thinks the Nailex (a proprietary name) has aniline in it, a severe poison which forms methemoglobin in replacement of hemoglobin and has a depressing effect on the central nervous system. Long term exposures do severe damage to the red blood cells and to the liver.

The traditional "blue lip" effect—turning blue around the lips and under the fingernails—shows up in the same plant from aniline exposure. Men showing this symptom are taken to a nearby hospital and treated until the condition is relieved.

Many do-it-yourself handymen who have done remodeling jobs on their homes are familiar with fiberglass insulation which may be purchased in long strips and are aware how tiny fragments of the fiberglass can cause itching of the skin. Imagine working all day in a factory which manufactures it!

In the plant of Fiberglas Canada, Limited, at Edmonton, Alberta, men who work in the final manufacturing stages and the packing of this product report many complaints with rashes. Curiously, it seems not to affect some men; others cannot endure it. Those who cannot accept the itching and irritation simply have to quit their jobs and seek employment elsewhere, according to Bruce Atchison, local union president. He reports the problem is much worse in the sweaty summer time, when men are tempted to take off long sleeved shirts and work in T-shirts. There is a wisecrack, not completely true, of course, that every fiberglass plant has at least one wildcat strike per summer as the men become overly irritated by the stuff.

The Edmonton plant also has a severe dust problem caused by the unloading, inside the plant building, of railroad hopper cars containing the various raw materials used to make the glass. Atchison says, "There's no exhaust ventilation at all in there. The only thing we can do is to open one of the warehouse doors." He adds that this is a rather chilly procedure on a Canadian winter day, "but there are some days we don't have too much choice." There is no evidence of undue health damage from the dusts in that plant; it just seems to be an unnecessarily miserable condition in which to work.

Employees of the sodium plant of Reactive Metals Incorporated, at Ashtabula, Ohio, are regularly irritated by smoke from self-igniting sodium. President Charles Thomas of the local union says: "You have spills here and there. This immediately ignites and this is where you get your smoke condition. The type of smoke from this is the type that if you just get it on your skin, it irritates the skin." Small wonder—the "smoke" is Na_2O—sodium oxide—and when breathed it immediately reacts with moisture in the respiratory system to form sodium hydroxide, or lye.

Asked the effect of this smoke on the respiratory system, Thomas says: "You don't breathe too good at all. I mean, it gets a severe coughing effect immediately." (Sax's "Dangerous Properties of Industrial Materials" says that sodium hydroxide has a markedly corrosive action on all body tissue. Its corrosive action on tissue causes burns and frequently deep ulceration, with ultimate scarring.)

Sodium and its compounds are quite common industrial materials. Extracted from brine (salt water) by an electrolysis process, sodium is used in compounds with other chemicals in a wide range of products, including many food additives. It is used as a reagent in processing various materials and in one process for making titanium. Common table salt, which is sodium chloride, is both a household product and an industrial chemical. Until chemically changed, salt is innocuous.

Harry Jacobs, who works in the Bound Brook, New Jersey, plant of Inmont Chemical, describes an annoyance often cited by workmen who deal with volatile products. "Some of these chemicals you actually take home on your breath," says Jacobs, "because if you go home and kiss your wife, she can smell it right away. Especially like cellosolve acetate, butylcellosolve and stuff like this."

The wife of E. W. Van Gunten, local union vice president in the Glidden plant in Cleveland, has a different way of determining if her husband has been working in Hylene, an organic diisocyanate used in the manufacture of polyurethane foam. "I have been married for 20 years and my wife can tell within five minutes after I get home whether I've been working with Hylene," Van Gunten declares. "I'm generally a peaceful man, I think, and right away I start fighting. She can tell me when I come home whether I've been in there and 99 times out of 100 she's right."

In a sickly humorous way, stories like these bring to mind the problem of the man who lingers too long at the bar and goes home with the smell of liquor on his breath. Some industrial fumes are intoxicating. Some send men on psychedelic trips. This fact, unfortunately, has come to the attention of youthful drug experimenters who sometimes burglarize warehouses to steal mind-blowing materials.

In the Inmont plant at Bound Brook, New Jersey, a man jumped off the top of a storage tank, apparently voluntarily, because he became intoxicated with toluene fumes. Toluene is a common component of model airplane glue, sometimes sniffed by teenagers.

John Carney, president of a local union of laboratory employees in the Sayreville plant of National Lead Company, says, "You start feeling woozy, dizzy, and you get a lot of people starting to sing like they were half loaded." Carney indicates that such artificial gayety is sometimes the first evidence of the presence of intoxicating fumes from paint solvents, because the men who work around these fumes regularly become insensitized to them and do not quickly smell their presence. Carney notes: "A lot of times you walk into the chloride department or into the paint lab and you say, 'Whew, boy, it stinks in here,' and the fellows in there can't smell it. I think you get used to it, you get used to the fumes and you can't smell them. If the danger point is when you can smell it, and you can't smell it any longer, you're in trouble."

In Edmonton, Alberta, Uniroyal operates a small plant for the manufacture of insecticides and herbicides. This United States-owned plant in Canada makes, among other things, some of the 2,4,5-T sprayed by the United States forces to kill vegetation in Vietnam. Arrangements were made for the author, ensconced in the Chateau Lacombe Hotel in Edmonton, to meet with two men from the Uniroyal plant. "Don't worry about recognizing them," said the friend who made the appointment, "you will smell them." The men came to the hotel immaculately scrubbed and wearing clean clothes not worn at work. The cloying smell of chlorophenols came into the room with them. These workmen said the smell, persisting despite repeated baths and use of perfumed aftershave lotions, was a constant source of embarrassment.

While some men endure insults to their sense of smell, others endure torture of their ears. Melvin Nothem, union chief steward of maintenance in the sodium plant of Reactive Metals, Incorporated, in Ashtabula, Ohio, wears a hearing aid in each ear. He is one of tens of thousands so affected by excessive noise in industry. Al Cheney, union president in the Amoco Canadian Petroleum sulfur extraction plant 30 miles from White Court in Alberta, is only 27 years old and has worked in the plant five years. His hearing is damaged. "The big thing is the sulfur plant," he explains. "They built us a control room, finally, after seven years of complaining. They never insulated it. So there's this fuel valve and the way the line is designed it screams like a bugger. It screams for eight hours a day. If you pick one thing you hate about that plant, it has to be that scream. It gets on your nerves."

There appears to be no financial limitation on the capacity of industrial management to maintain miserable working conditions. Money is the holy yardstick and, as an overly broad generalization, it might be said that the small companies pinch pennies harder. But the larger companies can be quite miserly, too, and they work from better technical bases which they use to create blizzards of confusion when the workmen ask for information.

Texaco is a corporation with $9.3 billion in assets, yet for three summer months in 1969 it neglected to repair the non-operative air conditioner in the laboratory of its huge Port Arthur, Texas, refinery. Ray Armstrong, a lab employee, says, "We objected to this because there are no windows in this laboratory, just doors. You open the door but the wind can't blow the draft right on through. You have stalls—in each room you have a stall that you work in and you have a hallway coming down. When you are working back in one of those stalls, the air is so heavy that the counter we work on has water on it."

Armstrong's dismay with the lack of air conditioning was not just a matter of temperature. "We use acids, we use toluol, benzene, carbon tetrachloride, aniline—just a number of chemicals. All this stuff we heat up and the vapors rise from it. The air was so heavy you could hardly breathe in there and everybody was walking around as if they had been running for about five miles—breathing hard," Armstrong continues. "You could go into town and buy circulating fans at one of those discount stores, for $10 to $15, but we couldn't even get fans! They wouldn't even go into town."

Eugene Charles, local union president, says of conditions in the U. S. Reduction Company plant at East Chicago, Indiana: "In our residue department, the dust is so thick 95 percent of the time that you cannot see your hands in front of your face." This plant melts down scrap aluminum, often covered with unknown residues, for re-use. "In our production department, the smoke and fumes are so bad that everyone in the department has to come out until the situation clears up," says Charles. "At times we have to wade in water. In the receiving department, our drying machine puts out so much smoke that the company only runs the machine at night so the smoke cannot be seen."

These are examples of industrial working conditions which, even if they have not been proven dangerous to health in an absolute and judicial sense, at best reflect miserable working conditions. Intolerable conditions? They are, in fact, tolerated, even though they should not be.

These are conditions behind the sparkling fronts, behind the neat office buildings which are behind the green front lawns characteristic of many modern industrial plants, behind the sparkling four-color magazine ads and clever television ads that purport to present American industry. The workmen spend their full eight hours—sometimes working a "double" to make it 16 hours—each day in the very middle of it all. The foremen, generally, have offices to which they can retreat. The next higher supervisors spend less time in the unpleasant places and have more remote offices. At each higher supervisory level, less time is spent in the actual plant until frequently, at the top level of plant management, entire weeks pass without any time spent in the operating section of the plant.

Managers are "too busy" making budgets, writing reports, engaging in company politics, explaining situations to the home office and otherwise playing the role of executive to fully involve themselves in some of the nitty-gritty of the plants they manage. Too often they really do not realize how unpleasant the conditions may be for their workmen.

Then, at a higher management level—well, toxic fumes and choking dust are quite rare in corporate board rooms.

4

Modern Ways to Die

Oil refinery workers worry about both quick death and slow death. Their concerns about slow death are vague: there are just too many heart attacks and too many cases of cancer, they think.

Quick death usually comes either from fire or brimstone. The fire danger is constant because an oil refinery processes vast volumes of liquid petroleum and petroleum products under high pressures and at high temperatures. Explosions and resulting fires can be sudden and violent.

Brimstone, as refinery workers endure it, is in the form of hydrogen sulfide gas (H_2S). Brimstone is the ancient name for sulfur, which in its common powdered form is good for roses. Sulfur combined with hydrogen forms hydrogen sulfide gas. It is offensive to the smell, corrosive to most anything, and a deadly respiratory irritant. It can deliver almost instant death or a wide variety of destructive slow injuries to human tissue. It is a major air pollutant.

Howard Thomas, 42, died in the Phillips Petroleum Company refinery in Kansas City, Kansas, in 1967. He was found at the foot of a ladder with his skull crushed. Since he had evidently fallen off the ladder, his death was attributed to a simple accident. Indications are, however, that he had climbed the ladder to a point within 40 or 50 feet of a sulfide vent stack off a sewer—a vent often emitting strong hydrogen sulfide fumes. Fellow workers think he fell from the ladder not because of carelessness, but because a sudden whiff of the H_2S gas rendered him unconscious.

Richard Bunting, described by his local union president, Robert Welman, as "an alert young fellow of good habits," was found at the foot of a ladder in the Ashland Oil Company refinery in Canton, Ohio, in September, 1967, his head crushed. Says Welman, "I know that this man was trained by one of the salaried people to bleed the H_2S right out into the open air when he was getting samples. He was trained to do this in order to get a more pure sample of the gas, which is a strict violation of safety procedures. We don't know that it happened that way, but anyway he was found at the bottom of the ladder." Bunting apparently had fallen from a platform several feet off the ground.

(Welman himself is partially blind. A few years ago, caustic soda sprayed into his face and eyes at the same refinery. An energetic, aggressive man, he lives on $49 per week workmen's compensation and the little extra money he earns doing organizing and special chores for the union.)

In April, 1968, an accident in the American Oil Company refinery at Texas City, Texas, resulted in three deaths and 14 injuries directly attributable to hydrogen sulfide. C. L. Lester, 28, and C. L. Wenning, 23, were sent to make a repair on a piece of refining equipment. It was supposedly clear of all fluids and gases, but somewhere along the line an error was made—H_2S in large volume was in the vessel. The two men unbolted a flange and the gas fogged out. They collapsed on a working platform 12 or 14 feet from the ground. Later appraisals were that they died instantly, but fellow workers who did not know this instinctively rushed to the rescue. One after another they approached the accident scene and collapsed of hydrogen sulfide asphyxiation.

An ambulance from a private ambulance service came on the scene, driven by a 20-year-old youth. Not knowing anything about the gas, this lad grabbed the supplemental oxygen bottle carried by the ambulance for such emergencies as heart attacks, donned the oxygen mask provided for such supplemental purposes, and started up the ladder. This device, not designed to keep anything out of the lungs, did not, of course, prevent him from inhaling the H2S; he fell from the ladder dead.

Altogether, 14 men were injured, several of them seriously enough to be hospitalized. One of them, Elton Young, was still having respiratory problems 10 months later. Many of those injured suffered needlessly. Training had not been provided for the men on the proper use of the self-breathing air masks provided for such emergencies.

Refinery fire can be equally gruesome. On October 1, 1969, Bobby Hayden and J. T. Freeman, pipefitters, were killed while making a repair near a unit of the Atlantic Richfield refinery in Houston, Texas, when a pipe ruptured and caused a flash fire.

This was a tube about eight inches in diameter carrying oil through a furnace—exposed to open flames in a firebox. The oil was under approximately 550 pounds per square inch pressure. "It just turned wrong side out," says Othel D. Newby, union chairman in the plant. "It's just hard to believe you could take a piece of pipe and turn it inside out." The rupture was about three feet long. An eight-inch jet of oil under high pressure poured into the fire box and burning oil spread around the immediate area. Workmen rushed forward, contained the fire within the area, closed valves to stop more oil from coming in.

The fire caught Hayden and Freeman. One of them had his clothing completely burned off. He was near death, but was still able to walk. There were no fire blankets whatsoever available to wrap him in, although subsequently blankets have been placed around the plant. The accident happened about 200 yards from the plant safety office, across a plant street from the fire house. This is a large refinery, employing between 1,500 and 2,000 people, but no one was manning the safety office on the night shift.

"One man was brought up to the front of the fire house," recalls Jack Stagner, union safety chairman. "The other staggered up there. There were these two men, fatally burned, and they were lying there begging somebody to help them. One of them was sitting on the side of a truck, the other one was lying on the street. They were just begging someone to help them when within less than 100 feet was the safety office—and not a soul there to operate the darn thing!"

This Atlantic Richfield refinery has an ambulance, but it does not—or at least did not at that time—make runs outside the plant. Hayden and Freeman waited until an outside ambulance came and hauled them away to a hospital where they died.

Some fatal fires are more predictable. W. R. Williamson, local union president, was killed and four workmen were injured in a fire about which there had been forewarning in the Texaco refinery in Casper, Wyoming, January 8, 1970.

A 55,000-barrel (2,310,000-gallon) asphalt storage tank had been emptied for the replacement of steam coils, which keep the thick, gummy asphalt liquefied in cold weather. At a coroner's inquest into Williamson's death, members of the local told how they had tried in vain to stop work inside the tank until it could be made safer. It was the workers' contention that the tank, which had been cleaned by an outside contractor's work force, still had too much asphalt residue remaining on the sides and bottom to be safe.

Don Dundas, union workmen's committee chairman, told the coroner's jury he had been alerted to the unsafe condition by electricians who had carried out the relatively safe job of installing temporary work lights inside the tank. The plant safety supervisor was on vacation. Dundas took the matter up with another company official, who inspected the tank and told the men: "The powers-that-be said they were going to do this job—the company needs the tank."

Welders at first refused to work in the tank; they feared that the fire from their torches would ignite the asphalt. After several days of controversy, and after sand was put on the floor, the welders reluctantly went to work. On two occasions, asphalt residue caught fire but the fires were put out with hand extinguishers. As late as the morning of the fire, Dundas again asked the refinery manager to stop work inside the tank until more of the residue could be cleaned out. The assistant refinery manager looked at the tank and once more gave the go-ahead.

That afternoon the residue again caught on fire. This time the blaze could not be put out with hand extinguishers. The men fled. Vapors inside the tank exploded just as those working inside reached an opening; they were blown clear. Three men were on top of the tank; two were blown clear by the force of the explosion but Williamson, the third man on top, was killed because he did not have time to unhook a safety harness intended to prevent his falling from the tank top.

Such explosions and fires are providentially infrequent in refineries, but the possibility of them puts the men under nervous strain. In recent, years, refinery workers have become more and more concerned about such dangers, because they believe that cost-cutting management is taking too many shortcuts on maintenance of equipment (as may have been the case in the Houston fire) and are not maintaining sufficiently large work forces for emergency situations. These views will be presented in more detail in Chapters 7 and 8.

The layman would think work in an explosives plant would be a most nerve-wracking occupation. There is, indeed, a high incidence of heart attacks in such plants, but the evidence is that these are caused by chemical exposure rather than tension. Johnny L. Cicero, union president in the DuPont explosives plant in Watson, Alabama, explains this. "You get where you accept the fact that this is an explosives plant and it can shoot," says Cicero. "You just learn to live with it. It's a calculated risk."

Each unit of an explosives plant is isolated from other units, to avoid chain reaction. Each building typically is barricaded strongly on three sides, left weak on a fourth side facing toward an open area. Therefore, if a building "shoots," as the workers refer to it, the force of the blast is channeled in one direction. A minimum number of men work in each unit.

Asked how many times in his 17 years in the DuPont plant there had been fatality-causing explosions, Cicero says, "Well, we have had two mix houses shoot and last time they had two people killed, the only two in the building." The earlier accident killed three, as Cicero recalls. Cicero wryly notes that there are no injuries from explosions. "You go all the way or not at all."

Cicero sums up, "Looking at the overall picture, it is the daily consumption of fumes that would hurt more people than would an explosion." He describes reactions to glycol, a base ingredient for explosives. "You inhale it," he explains. "The fumes create—well, you get a headachy effect from this immediately. You can feel it in your pulse, in your armpits, in your temples and the back of your neck."

Does your pulse speed up?

"Yes, it seems like it is stronger, and greater. You can feel your heart beat faster, seems like harder, especially in your armpits. It's not exactly a speed-up maneuver, it's that the sensation is harder. In damp, wet weather, and also in the summer months, you feel the sensation a lot more than you do in winter months. Could be that the pores are more open, and that way you get more of the fumes into the body, into the bloodstream." Cicero asserts that the average man in the plant is likely to feel the reaction nearly every day, to some extent.

"It's hard to get some doctors to make statements about what being in an exposed area will do to you," says Cicero. "I think all of them know what damage nitroglycerine can do to you, by working in it daily. But as for getting any doctor just to make a point blank statement that it will injure your health, I haven't had anybody do that yet."

Many workers in the plant are convinced that the exposures do cause heart damage. "We have a good many heart attacks at our plant," Cicero says. Then he adds a curious note which indicates that he means "among workers of the plant" rather than "at the plant." He says, "I don't think we have ever had a man have a heart attack in the plant—with one exception. One man did die in the plant. Most of the heart attacks come after a man has had a vacation period or was off on a weekend. On the one occasion I talked about, the one man did die inside the plant. He came back from a weekend, to work on Monday. He didn't make it back to his job location; he sat down under a tree and died."

Cicero continues: "A majority of them have heart attacks when they are away from the plant. I guess—some doctors have indicated—that if a man could get back to work and breathe some of those fumes, he wouldn't have a heart attack." Cicero thinks a lot of the retired men take nitroglycerine pills, since they don't have the sustaining crutch of plant fumes to keep their hearts stimulated at the above normal levels to which they have become accustomed. "We have an awful lot of young men having attacks—men under 40, anywhere from 37 to 39 years old," Cicero concludes.

Carbon monoxide and chlorine are the fumes most disabling in the National Lead Company in Sayreville, New Jersey. The product of the plant is titanium pigment for paints—a pigment which has in substantial measure replaced the poisonous lead of earlier day paints. Chlorine and carbon monoxide are used in the manufacturing process. The local union there has recorded something over half a hundred cases of gassing by either carbon monoxide or chlorine in a period of about 18 months ending in late 1969.

In addition to Jimmy Owen, whose death in the plant was noted in Chapter 1, the local union believes one other death of a young man resulted from carbon monoxide exposures. Gene Morton died outside the factory of a cerebral hemorrhage. Suspicion lingers because Morton had been exposed to the gas and because the gas can do brain damage. It has an affinity for hemoglobin in the blood 210 times greater than that of oxygen. By combining with the hemoglobin, the carbon monoxide deprives the blood of its oxygen-carrying capacity. The brain is quickly and irreparably damaged if deprived of oxygen. Cerebral hemorrhage frequently strikes elderly people, but is rare among people in their twenties like Gene Morton.

Local President Peter McIntyre* adds: "We had another young fellow by the name of Carmen Perno who also suffered, if I remember correctly, a cerebral hemorrhage and spent a long time in the hospital. He has returned to work and is doing a normal job." President John Carney of the local union of laboratory workers in the same plant reports, "I myself have had pneumonia three of the last four years and three times in one year. They attributed it back to the fumes in the lab."

President William Bowers of the local representing employees of J. T. Baker Chemical Company at Phillipsburg, New Jersey—the small plant that lists nearly 6,000 chemicals in its sales catalog—offhand names three fellow workers who are seeking workmen's compensation on the grounds that they suffered lung damage from fumes breathed in the plant. He names Al Bowers, Bernie Cacklin and Art Miller. He adds that another man who works in a department where hundreds of chemicals are subdivided for packaging, has been off work with a nervous breakdown and thinks it is attributable to fumes he has breathed in the plant.

In addition to Thurman Wooten, mentioned in Chapter 1, John Tipton, 54, was told by his doctor in the fall of 1969 to quit working at the Farmers Chemical Company plant in Joplin, Missouri. After a few weeks away from the job, Tipton felt better. "Now, I've been off work about 10 weeks and I'm getting pretty good. Lot better than what it was. Used to couldn't sleep at nights; had to sleep in a chair. If I lay down on my back I'd start coughing and couldn't breathe. I had an ulcer on the top of my stomach, the doctor says from breathing (sulfuric acid) fumes. So the doctor told me absolutely to get out. I'm getting out."

---

* Since providing this information, McIntyre has left the office of local union president. All titles and job identification used in this book are those effective as of the time information was given, not necessarily applicable at time of writing.

Tipton and Wooten were perhaps more fortunate than A. E. McClelland. The afternoon of July 7, 1968, he was hooking up a hose to unload a tank car of sulfuric acid—one of the many brimstone products—in the Kansas City refinery of Phillips Petroleum. His helper testified that he had vented the car to relieve the pressure, but nevertheless when the car was opened sulfuric acid burped out, hit him just below the chin, and covered between 90 and 95 percent of his body. "He's nothing but one mass of scars," says local union President Ray Lovelady. "He was off work 13 months, but now we do have him back on limited duty."

Was there an emergency shower nearby, under which McClelland could quickly flush off the acid?

Lovelady: "Was there a safety shower? I'm glad you asked that. This unloading spot had been there 17 years. Immediately beside this spot there had been a shower for 15½ years. The company completed a modernization program in 1965 in which they built another acid unloading spot approximately 200 yards to the east, where they unloaded hydrofluoric acid. I guess this was considered to be a little more dangerous, so they moved the shower stall from the sulfuric acid spot, leaving the sulfuric unloading area with no water at all, not even a water hose. Mac had to run 75 to 80 yards to get to a water hose."

The normal period of "grace" in which a man can avoid injury by flushing off sulfuric acid is 30 seconds. Time aside, the hose McClelland reached probably was inadequate. Suitable safety showers for men subject to exposure to acids and other burning agents are activated by a quick yank on a rope or chain, rather than by the slower process of opening a valve. They pour a deluge of water, not just a spray, on the man. The man is supposed to strip naked quickly as possible after getting under the water. Some showers are so arranged that pulling the cord to turn the shower on activates an alarm horn or bell to summon help.

"They moved this shower instead of building another,"

Lovelady continues. "We begged them, in monthly meetings. We begged them. I don't mean we waited until the monthly meeting. We talked to them whenever we saw a supervisor around the plant, 'Don't move that shower, build another one.' We begged them to do this."

Sulfuric acid is one of the most widely used and dangerous industrial chemicals. In strengths above 93 percent, and including the various oleums, it is violently corrosive. Its action on the flesh is by dehydration. It has such a strong affinity for water—one of its many industrial uses is as a "drying agent"—that it literally draws water from the flesh, charring it beyond repair. The burns are painful, long-lasting and frequently require skin grafts. Yet, in tank trucks sulfuric acid moves about our highways and city streets as casually as milk from the farm—hundreds of loads every day.

A listing of industrial deaths and serious injuries could be endless; those given are examples. Some of the deaths and accidents are listed in official statistics, some are not. When a man dies as the direct and visible result of a traumatic accident, he is listed. When a man is injured, visibly, in the plant, he may or may not be listed as a "lost-time accident."

When a man is made ill by working conditions, he most likely is not listed. And those who gradually, imperceptibly, weaken have virtually no recognition at all of their problems.

5

As Through a Glass, Darkly

A devoted local union officer and a distinguished medical doctor address themselves eloquently to their frustrations in contending with industrial health hazards.

Peter McIntyre, president of the union in the National Lead Company plant at Sayreville, New Jersey, discusses exposures in his plant, especially exposures to carbon monoxide and chlorine gases. He lists case after case of workmen overcome by the gases. When asked "Do you think you've cited some of the more serious cases?" McIntyre replies: "Well, we can't even determine if they're the more serious, because all of them are serious. It's only a question of to what degree. Now, if we sit here and we're healthy and calm we could very easily say that this case is more severe than that case. But the individual who has difficulty breathing because of chlorine gassing might not agree.

"Number 1, the man can't get his breath. Number 2, he has chest pains or thickening of the chest. Number 3, the back of his neck is sore—it may be because of coughing. Number 4, he has a sore throat. Number 5, sometimes he feels sick for days. Number 6, the upper respiratory tract suffers from infection. Number 7, he has a slight pressure for several hours afterward in his chest. Number 8, he goes through vomiting. Number 9, dizziness. Number 10, he has headaches. Number 11, blurred eye vision. Number 12, loss of memory in some cases. With carbon monoxide, they suffer from most all of these, plus in the case where it was claimed—and we feel— that it resulted in a brain hemorrhage.

"Now, the treatment. Some of it is with oxygen, some with fresh air. They have a peppermint cough syrup. They have a penicillin needle and they have a chest X-ray. We hesitate to say that any one of these cases is average, but I'm sure my wife and two sons would suffer if I went home with any of these 12 symptoms. Any one of these symptoms is going to make me an unpleasant person to live with."

Speaking from another viewpoint, from the dark, back side of the autopsy report, is Dr. Hawey A. Wells, Jr., director of the Pulmonary Research Laboratory at the Conemaugh Valley Memorial Hospital in Johnstown, Pennsylvania. Dr. Wells testifies before the Select Subcommittee on Labor of the U. S. House of Representatives on March 14, 1968:

"I am a pathologist and as a pathologist I study the mechanisms of disease by examination of tissues. The mechanics of disease and death means each significant step between the first cause and the final effect of any process that causes death. I am used to having the last word in medical conferences because I have the added advantage of clinical information concerning the causes under consideration plus the final look into the body, into the tissue, that defines the disease.

"Pathology's contribution came after thousands of years of guesswork into the workings of disease on the human body. When we were at last permitted to make complete examination of the human body, to lay the organs out in the open and to study them completely, we were finally able to come out of the dark ages and allow the great advances that medicine has made in prevention, in diagnosis and in curing disease.

"The same applies in industrial health. We can only hope to be able to diagnose or cure industrial problems when we can completely analyze the industrial environment that caused the injury, the disease or the death."

Describing his frustration as a physician searching for the true cause of each death, Dr. Wells continues:

"Each day I examine mangled arms and legs or fingers, hands, lungs, spleens, bladders, cancers of all sorts and disease, and I try to diagnose the primary cause *without the basic information necessary.* (Emphasis added.)

"We have to look more deeply into the environment, into the conditions that initiate the processes [of death]. Even those most vigorously opposed to H.R. 14816* admit that we don't know enough about the cause of accidents, about the cause of disease and death in industry. If everybody is in favor of research or at least does not openly oppose research and education, *let's make sure that this research is complete research, that it includes the right to examine the environment as well as the disease, to enter any industry engaged in interstate commerce and using potentially dangerous caustic materials so that we can make that complete examination.* (Emphasis added.)

"In my personal research, I study the effect of particulates, tiny particles of dust of various kinds, upon the lungs. There is a big block in this field, a big frustration for all of the workers. There is an impossible task of correlating the disease that we find at autopsy with the work environment. We have to try to guess at what the work environment was that caused it. We never know the duration of exposure, the exact chemical nature or the particle sizes or the concentrations."

Conscientious physicians such as Dr. Wells are handicapped by a lack of adequate information as they try to diagnose illnesses. The frustrations of industrial workers, while more vague and less scientific, certainly are no less poignant.

Emphysema, rare a few years ago, is crippling and killing thousands of Americans. Smoking of tobacco is thought to be at least a contributing cause of this lung ailment. It is difficult to blame smoking entirely, however, since heavy smokers have been around much longer than heavy incidence of emphysema. There is room for suspicion that the general air pollution of the current era contributes, or perhaps there is a synergistic effect when people both smoke and breathe polluted air.

Industrial workers who spend 40 hours per week inside

---

* A health and safety bill considered in 1968.

plants heavily polluted by fumes and dusts are particularly uneasy. They get little guidance from the medical profession. Harvey Cowan, now 54, retired from work three years ago with a serious case of emphysema. Admittedly, a heavy smoker before the disease was diagnosed, Cowan sincerely believes that conditions in his work place caused, or substantially contributed to, his disability. He was employed in the molecular sieve department of the Tonawanda, New York, plant of Linde Division of Union Carbide Corporation.

A molecular sieve is not akin to the gadgets found in kitchens. It is a powdered or beaded compound of chemicals having extraordinary capacity to adsorb water or other materials; a little of it between the sheets of glass in a double-paned window helps eliminate annoying moisture condensation. Aluminum trihydrate, caustic and other materials are involved in its manufacture.

"I worked in that department," Cowan relates. "I was a chemical operator. Conditions were very, very bad. The dust accumulated all over the plant. If you banged a pipe or anything, just a cloud floated down. The duct system originally was put in there for some other purpose. I was constantly at odds with management about the fact that the dust wasn't being taken out, wasn't being removed. I think one of the big factors in it was the bead machine. You are constantly feeding dry powder onto a bed that is rolling through a drum and you are spraying liquid on top of it, an air and liquid spray, and this dust is constantly coming out of this drum.

"The ventilation ducts were always plugged up—well, not always, but a good part of the time. They would hook up an air hose in order that you could operate the machine. One man had to stand right there at one end of the drum while operating it, and in order to operate it you had to have an air hose there to kind of blow it through the back. We would wire the hose up on a piece of equipment so that it would be constantly blowing in the drum to keep the dust out of our faces.

"On top of that, you had other processes with these beads.

You had to go around back of this machine. Of course, you were inhaling all of this stuff that you had been blowing out of the back of this drum. I know many times I came out of there and it just felt like my lungs were solid."

Harvey Cowan could be an isolated case, but other employees of the molecular sieve department have had serious ailments, too. George Roehrig died in 1969 while on total and permanent disability retirement with emphysema. Harold Michle was asking for workmen's compensation for emphysema in mid-1970. Chris Steurnagel has been off work since December, 1969, with emphysema. Joseph Shoemaker suffers from the same ailment.

John Morrill has chronic bronchial disease. Charles Robinson has emphysema, poor circulation in the legs and ulcers on the legs caused by caustic fumes; he was off work several weeks early in 1970 and now has moved out of the department. R. Whitfield has ulcers on the legs. Joseph Mahoney was told by his doctor to move out of the molecular sieve department because of dermatitis. Because he has a large family to support, he has not moved. Jack Pettit still works in the department, although he has dermatitis.

Don Kreuter, local union trustee, told a U. S. Senate committee hearing in May, 1970, that of 18 men in the molecular sieve department, seven have emphysema, two have circulatory problems in their legs and two have dermatitis. He thinks each man in the department has had dermatitis at one time or another.

"The duct systems are poor. There is improper ventilation throughout the plant," say Kreuter. The men are advised by management to wear simple little felt filter masks, if the dust bothers them. Kreuter says these clog up in five minutes.

Emphysema worries the men in the American Cyanamid plant at Kalamazoo, Michigan, because three men out of a work force of 29 have been incapacitated by lung diseases in three years. At least two of these men are known to have emphysema. Local union president Lawrence Pease lists the three as Ray Douglas, who was off duty two years before returning to work as a truck driver, and Ralph Edens and Johnny Hambright, who had been off work on disability about a year as of February, 1970. Edens was retired on total and permanent disability; Hambright was requesting permanent retirement on disability.

Pease does not know whether physicians attributed these illnesses to exposures to injurious materials at work. "You get exposed to just about everything in that plant," Pease comments.

On the subject of gas exposures in the sodium plant of Reactive Metals, Incorporated, in Ashtabula, Ohio, local union president Charles Thomas says that "very seldom do you go by a day without a man getting a dose." He says that between January 1 and June 1, 1970, there were 117 gas cases reported to the first aid room. Secretary Albert Nist of the local extrapolates these daily, painful experiences into a long-term concern. "The guys have more or less learned to live with it," he says. "After being down there 20 years, I know all those guys and I know what they looked like when they started there. I would say that the men that I started with 20 years ago have aged considerably up in the sodium shop—more than I have." (Nist works in a different department). "You can tell by their skin, by their complexion."

Melvin Nothem, chief steward in the maintenance department of the same shop, worries about long-term effects of fumes from welding of various metals. "One fellow—Neil Ferguson—had half a lung removed. He's back to work, but they put him right back on the same job, welding nickel, constantly," says Nothem. "And on the other side of the same department they've got two men with emphysema real bad due to the fact that both of them are resilvering bases. They heat these bases red hot and they put this silver on them, and the fumes—you can hardly see them working in it. The smoke and fumes are so bad and the exhaust system they have there wouldn't take cigaret smoke out of the building."

Nothem says the two men had emphysema "due to the fact both of them are resilvering bases." Of course he cannot prove that. This is the frustration of it all.

Nothem and others are concerned. It seems to them that precautions should be taken. But Nothem's frustrations are heightened when he complains to management. "They keep saying, 'We'll look into it.' They pass the buck. Then they come in with a two-dollar outfit that wouldn't be adequate for cigaret smoke and they expect it to take these fumes out. You can't spend a few nickels, you've got to spend a few dollars if you're going to take care of this situation," Nothem says. "The company realizes this. They just sit there and deny it, about the emphysema cases and the conditions we got down there."

Local Union President Roy Barnes speaks of somewhat more vague concerns in the Shell Oil refinery and contiguous Shell Chemical plant at Pasadena, Texas. "I don't have any figures to back it up, but it seems to me there are more heart attacks and more lung ailments, more pneumonia, more lung cancer than the regular population has," says Barnes.

L. E. Sanford, an employee of the lubricating oils department of the refinery, adds: "I'm like Roy, I don't have any figures. I'd like to see some figures on it, to see whether we have more lung ailments in Shell than we do in other companies around. I believe that we do. I could name a few people who have had serious lung surgery out there. I can recall Wilkers and Glitcher and Miller, just three I know of real well. Yes, and Hunter."

P. V. Womack of the Shell refinery says: "We had two staff people in our department die with lung cancer." Sanford continues, "Had two die with lung cancer. We have one off now with cancer of the throat from our department. When I say 'our department,' I'm talking about 60 or 70 people."

Nelson Edgerly, union chairman in the Texaco refinery at Port Arthur, Texas, tells of an informal report he heard from a company doctor. "It is my understanding that the results of a study he made showed 10 percent of the employees at Texaco had some type of heart condition or heart disease. If you want to go into this statistically, look at the number of people who hadn't been out there long enough, or young people who wouldn't have been affected by conditions in the plant. Well, this greatly increases the percentage of heart conditions of people of age, say 35 to 40, and on up to retirement age."

Edgerly's fears are vague, unprovable. But the fear gnaws. Edgerly draws the distinction between provable accidents and vague illnesses. "We had a man out there handling a chemical who just happened to be standing over a ditch when the chemical ate the bottom of the galvanized bucket out. The chemical hit the water. Nobody really knew at that time what the reaction would be. It didn't do anything but cover him up with foam and gas. He got some in his nose and it ate the bone out of his nose. The company recognized this as an industrial accident and they had to put in a plastic nose."

But slower exposures are harder to evaluate. "We have people who have to take the physical as far as benzene and toluene are concerned," notes Edgerly. "I don't think that the tests that are given these people are really appropriate for the exposure they are getting. All they go on is blood count. As long as that doesn't change, then everything is all right. We don't know what type of effect it is going to have on other organs of the body. It might be working on him. All these things we don't know, and nobody else knows, I guess, as to what is going to happen.

"Where you are exposed to these toxic materials over a number of years . . . well, the old boy died of a heart attack. We don't know what correlation they have there. Or he died of cancer of the lungs. Or they cut him open and he was eaten up by cancer or what have you, or deterioration of the bone structure. We don't know. This is the thing that worries us more than anything else."

Ray Armstrong of the laboratory of the same refinery adds: "We are getting all those samples in there. They'll come marked in code numbers. You don't know what they are. Our people have to heat them up to make blends or run flash tests. You get it on your hands where it gets into your pores, or gets into your blood stream, or the marrow of your bones, or whatever. You ask any questions of management, why, they don't know themselves what it is."

In the Delta Match Company factory near New Orleans, an unusual amount of illness occurs in one department, where a large percentage of the employees are women. Women often call in saying that they "don't feel well." More substantial illnesses are reflected in the exceedingly high rate of claims under the group insurance policy for hospital and medical care.

Nedas Gauthreaux, local union president, says that nervous disorders are the most common complaints. In addition, some employees working in the area where the match sticks are dipped, mechanically, into the material which makes the striking head, suffer from skin rashes. Gauthreaux says that the company has often complained about excessive absenteeism in the department, making assertions to the effect that "it seems like we have all our bad apples in this department."

But it was in this same department that the company has had numerous malfunctions of micro-switches—delicate devices which rapidly open and close electrical circuits to operate machinery. The same type switches served normally in other departments. The company asked engineers from the company which manufactures the micro-switches to check the problems. These engineers studied the situation and expressed the opinion that chemicals in the air were causing excessive corrosion of the instruments.

If chemicals foul up the instruments, Gauthreaux wonders if they may not also be fouling up the people. But there is no medical information to clarify the matter.

Employees in the Glidden varnish and paint plant in Cleveland, Ohio, are, to put it in the vernacular, just plain bugged by Hylene. Hylene is a proprietary trade name. The Gardner and Cooke dictionary, "Chemical Synonyms and Trade

Names," lists four forms—Hylene, Hylene B, Hylene C and Hylene D. Some of these are plasticizers used to contribute flexibility and strength to plastics. Modern varnishes often are forms of liquid plastic.

Says Nick Kostandaras, president of the local union representing Glidden employees: "Hylene, as we have been told by doctors, is a type of chemical that accumulates in your system and every time you get it, it gets worse and worse. I can speak for one guy, not to mention his name, I think he has gotten a little bit nervous. And I think that some of the people in that department are coming down with some sickness and actually they don't know that the sickness they are getting is a result of chemicals that they use in the department."

What kind of sicknesses do they seem to be having?

Kostandaras: "Colds, your teeth, your eyes."

What's the problem with the teeth?

"Losing of the teeth, pyorrhea. And stomach problems, such as ulcers."

George Woytko, union grievance chairman, adds: "They always seem to have a different complexion. Their complexions seem to be paler. And it's not only that it bothers you in breathing. It's dangerous to handle. One time one of the drums exploded and flew up and hit a rail near the ceiling and wrapped itself around that rail and just hung there suspended." A co-worker says that moisture had gotten into the drum and caused a violent reaction.

The unknowns of the jungle always are more frightful than the known dangers of familiar ground. The concern with Hylene is reflected in a story told by E. W. Van Gunten, local union vice president: "I walked up to the elevator with this fellow. You could see him starting to gasp. And I said, it must be Hylene. He starts to cough a little, he starts to gasp, and he stands there no more than three minutes and we got him into the first aid room.

"We told them (in first aid) it was Hylene odor. They said, 'Oh, no, there's no Hylene in there, none in that building.'

We went over there and checked and there had been a drum in there a day or two before and they spilled some on the floor. It was laying there by the elevator and this is just how fast it affected him." The man was hospitalized for about three days.

Men are subject to uncertainty and strain when making commonplace products like varnish. The same is true—and perhaps the strain is no worse—among those working with more esoteric products. Eddie Nichols works in the Goodyear Atomic Company plant in Piketon, Ohio. Radiation is a matter of concern there—but not the only one.

Says Nichols: "I've seen men die," and he adds that besides radiation there are such chemicals as chlorine, fluorine and nickel carbonyl. "I've had an experience with nickel carbonyl. All I know about it is that you can't smell it, you can't see it, yet it's there. This is what I'm concerned about, mostly. These are things you can't fight people about when you don't know what they are. It's the unseen things that really scare me."

One employee of this plant was severely burned on the chest by liquid fluorine, a very powerful acidic agent. After treatment, he returned to work, then died in the plant two weeks later of a heart attack. Did the fluorine burn have a bearing? Nichols does not know.

The testimony of the workers is vague. The layman hearing them might at first be contemptuous. Why, he might ask, do these men stumble around in ignorance? The answer is that the ignorance extends to high places. The Surgeon General's report, "Protecting the Health of Eighty Million Americans," says, "Little is known of the subtle effects of chronic, low-level exposure to industrial poisons." The report adds, "New scientific knowledge points to hitherto unsuspected cause-and-effect relationships between occupational exposures and many of the so-called chronic diseases—cancer, respiratory ailments, allergies, heart diseases and others."

Emil Peter, local union secretary, is concerned about the 100 products that are shipped into, stored, sometimes blended, and shipped out of General American Transportation Company's big storage and transfer facility at Carteret, New Jersey.

General American—GATX, for short—specializes in providing contract transfer and storage services for oil companies, supplying railroad tank cars, storage tanks and other facilities. In recent years, it has branched out into handling all sorts of chemicals, particularly those in liquid form.

In the Carteret facility are such things as methanol, acetone, toluene, vinyl acetate, formic acid, bromine, butanol, brucine, sulfuric acid, acetic anhydride, ethylenediamine, phenol, cumene, tetrahydrofuran, propionic acid, butyl acetate, isopropane, nicotine, acetaldehyde.

Are there deaths and sicknesses in the plant attributable to exposure to these? Emil Peter says, "There is no scientific or medical proof of this. However, I'll give you an opinion. By observation, it seems to me that respiratory ailments are on the upswing in our plant. Within the last year and a half we've had three people who did not reach retirement age—they died somewhere between 62 and 65.

"We've got some people who are chronic absentees, and I don't mean in the sense that they're problem employees. It's just that they physically can't get themselves to work in the morning. If we would exchange views down there, if we would say, 'How do you feel today?' a lot of the people would say, 'I got a lousy headache', 'I have a chest constriction', 'My pains are terrible', 'I just feel nauseous', 'I haven't got any appetite'."

Don Courtney, an intense, intelligent 26-year-old union committeeman in the Wyandotte Chemical Company plant at Baton Rouge, Louisiana, says: "Many of our young people are really concerned about what effect our work conditions have on health. They know that they're being exposed to hazardous atmospheres and they're alarmed. They are becoming a great deal concerned about what effect this is going to have on them. Already, some of them say they don't feel as good as they did when they came there. These are people of my age, 26 and maybe a year or two older or younger."

Some of Courtney's complaints are more specific. "My nasal passages are stopped up today. This is Saturday, and this comes from being exposed to chlorine on Thursday. And I continue to keep a cold. I have various treatments, cold remedies, but none works in chlorine."

Local union President Leo Reidel speaks with somewhat more agitation of the situation in the American Oil Company refinery at Texas City, Texas. Hands trembling, he waves a slip of paper and says, "I have here a list of the names of 18 hourly rated employees. Out of these 18 names, four of them are dead from lung cancer. This is the period from 1961 through 1968."

Who are the four dead of lung cancer?

Reidel: "I hope I have the spelling correct here. Robert Sherrod, an operator; Harold Dyer, he was a laborer; Tay Bishop, he was a pipefitter; Tommy Frasier, an instrument man. Those men are dead. Now these others on this list either have had surgery on their lungs or extremely serious respiratory diseases. I know that lost time for respiratory ailments in the refinery has been on a steady climb for a number of years. Management even admits this."

The conversation is interrupted; other members of the local chat with Reidel. He resumes: "We have come up with Wally Steel, dead from lung cancer, and Frank Salina is dead from lung cancer. I have also the names of Brother R. G. Gist, Brother A. O. Logan, Brother Paul Naquin. These three brothers have all had at least a portion of their lungs removed by surgery. These are in addition to the first list."

Reidel can prove nothing. He just thinks there is too much of a pattern of death in the refinery where workers breathe various hydrocarbon fumes, hydrogen sulfide and other gases, and what Harold Hardage of the contiguous Amoco Chemical plant refers to as "so damn many chemicals they quit printing the hazardous code book . . . they quit printing them; I think they're scared to." In desperation, Reidel waves his sheet of paper and begs for light on the subject.

Local union President Ray Lovelady's long feud with Phillips Petroleum Company regarding undue incidence of cancer and leukemia deaths among employees of the company's Kansas City refinery led to a series of contradictions before a Congressional committee in which the Phillips company doctor came out second best.

For some years, Lovelady pestered management with inquiries about the frequency of cancer cases. Finally he went to several county recorders' offices and extracted death certificates on fellow workers who had died. Anthony Mazzocchi, Citizenship-Legislative Director of Oil, Chemical and Atomic Workers International Union, referred to these deaths in testimony before a Congressional committee on March 7, 1968. He mentioned 17 deaths from cancer and leukemia among 400 Phillips' employees in a period of 12 years. These figures might have been passed over as insignificant, but Phillips over-reacted.

A memorandum by Dr. Keiffer Davis, medical director of the company, was submitted to the committee for its records. Dr. Davis wrote: "During the 12-year period referred to by Mr. Mazzocchi there were three deaths of employees from cancer, one of the throat and two of the lungs, and one death from leukemia. During this 12-year period, of the 138 individuals who have retired from this refinery, 25 are deceased, one had leukemia, one female office worker had carcinoma of the breast, and one had aplastic anemia.

"None of these people," Dr. Davis added with emphasis, "had worked in areas of the refinery where even a potential exposure to hydrogen sulfide or any other hydrocarbon was possible."

To this, Lovelady responded by submitting to the committee 16 death certificates, one short of Mazzocchi's testimony showing deaths by cancer and leukemia. There have been additional deaths since the period covered by Lovelady's documentation.

The union spokesmen probably erred on the low side in referring to the number of employees as 400. Over the entire period in question, the average number was somewhat higher. But the minor errors made in the union testimony, and the questionable significance of the number of deaths, are more than offset by the incredibly defensive attitude of management.

Dr. Davis' assertion that "none of these people had worked in areas of the refinery where even a potential exposure to hydrogen sulfide or any other hydrocarbons was possible" reflects either that this medical man had never stuck his nose within a mile of the plant or that he simply was not telling the truth. The degree of exposure may be debatable, but hydrocarbon smells are constantly present in and around all oil refineries and hydrogen sulfide fumes are not uncommon.

Even the woman who worked in the office could not have entirely escaped these fumes, although there certainly is no indication that they might have caused breast cancer, for air conditioning intakes or open windows inevitably would have brought the fumes into the office building. The fact that some form or other of sulfur fumes are endemic in the refinery is proven by the fact that silver coins carried inside the pockets of workmen frequently are discolored. This phenomenon is commonplace in oil refineries.

Attitudes such as those displayed by Dr. Davis contribute substantially to the touchiness of industrial workers. To put it bluntly, they simply have little faith in what the bosses and company doctors say on the subject of health hazards.

A more precise set of figures is provided by local union President Percy Ashcraft regarding the health of his fellow workers in Union Carbide Corporation's Clarksburg, West Virginia, plant, which manufactures electrodes and anodes by processes similar to those described in an earlier reference to Carborundum Company's Hickman, Kentucky, facility. Around Clarksburg, the local wisecrack is, "You don't need road directions to reach the Carbide plant—just drive toward that pall of smoke."

Ashcraft says, "I have worked at Carbide since 1943 and I've watched conditions continually get worse. Since 1963, I've kept records and I've found that our disability retirements exceed normal retirements by two to one. Last year (1969) we had four normal retirements (at age 65), four early retirements and six disability retirements. Last year we had five deaths in our ranks from 'natural causes' and two of these were men from the impregnating department, in their early fifties, who died of lung cancer. We asked management recently to permit us to monitor dust and fume conditions, but they turned us down. The company said they would let us know if they found any hazards."

Union Carbide is not likely to find out the extent of hazards. The years have passed without it doing so. This company operates 280 manufacturing plants in the United States and Canada, at last count, and if it has made much effort to study the subject, this fact has escaped the attention of the employees.

Union Carbide is not alone. The nation does little to lighten the dark glass through which worried workers view their future health prospects. A. C. Blackman, managing director of the American Society of Safety Engineers, told a U. S. Senate committee on June 12, 1968, just how little is being done in industrial health and safety research.

"It is of interest to note," he said, "that in 1966 a total of $23 billion was spent for research and development work in the United States. Of this total only $7.5 million was being devoted to accident research."

One dollar of each three thousand! But, wait. Blackman testified further: "A total of 147 research projects were identified and described. *Of these, 24 were non-motor vehicle accident projects.* Five of the 24 projects were being undertaken by one large casualty insurance company, eight did not indicate the amount of funds expended. Eleven were funded at a total cost of $350,000."

Other fuzzy figures could be cited and the confusion would

be compounded. All in all, it is doubtful that federal, state and local agencies plus all insurance companies and employers combined spend as much as 10 cents per year on health hazard research for each of the 80 million Americans who work for a living.

Again and again we find ourselves inadvertently slipping into these statistical observations yet they fail to tell the story. The real area of concern has to do with individual human beings—tall, short, stout or skinny—that we know. We have to think of Fred Mosher, a promising young union leader, and Jim Campbell, a quiet, steady veteran, who work in Shell Chemical Company's insecticide plant near Denver, Colorado, and of Dick Eckenroth, David Towler and 150 other men who work there.

These men were subjects of a medical research project on the effect on the brain and nervous system of organophosphorus and chlorinated hydrocarbon exposures. The project has been aborted for lack of funds. Questions are left hanging, half-finished findings are left dangling.

Dr. David R. Metcalf, director of electroencephalogram research, department of psychiatry, University of Colorado Medical Center, carried on the project for seven years with the aid of a grant from the U. S. Public Health Service. Such research is tedious. Volunteers from the work force submitted to repeated tests, not only commonplace laboratory tests but also fat biopsies, EEG tests and psychological examinations. Sometimes the men went to bed with the EEG wiring attached to their heads to test brain functions during sleep.

"Just speaking for myself," say Eckenroth, union chairman in the plant, "I've had electroencephalograms. They've put me to sleep. I've had urine samples, blood samples. Had a biopsy taken off my body. I went to a psychologist. I put blocks together, looked at everything just like I was in a looney house. I went through the whole thing. You see, for seven years they ran these tests on a hundred of our people out there."

The project began with three-way cooperation between the

medical center, the Shell company and the union. Some of the workers think Shell management became reluctant in its cooperation. Eckenroth says: "The company decided they'd gone too far because Metcalf was running up stuff on abnormal brain patterns. Like we'd have a bad aldrin spill, or a bad dieldrin spill, or we'd rupture a disk* in a unit. Soon as we'd have an over-exposure, they'd run an EEG on us. They'd find abnormality in the brain, or something. They'd pull us out of the unit. We wouldn't be exposed to it anymore and it would clear up."

No cases can be found in which men such as those alluded to by Eckenroth were referred to Dr. Metcalf's research team for EEG tests after over-exposure, although the company knew that he had made his facilities available for EEG testing, psychological testing and medical evaluation at no cost to any employee for which there was a suspected need.

Dr. Metcalf and Dr. Joseph H. Holmes of the University of Colorado Medical Center have published some cautiously worded reports on their research. Also covered by their studies are certain employees of the Army's Rocky Mountain Arsenal who are exposed to organophosphorus in the making and handling of nerve gas. The Shell insecticide facility operates within this arsenal, using facilities leased from the government. One paper published by Drs. Metcalf and Holmes appeared in the June 23, 1969 issue of "Annals of the New York Academy of Sciences." Entitled "EEG, Psychological and Neurological Alterations in Humans with Organophosphorus Exposure," its findings are limited and tentative.

Regarding psychological tests, the report says, "Results indicate that the dysfunctions most clearly seen in the exposed group are disturbed memory and difficulty in maintaining alertness and appropriate focusing of attention. There is more usage

---

* To "rupture a disk" means to cause the breaking of a "rupture disk" in a reactor or other vessel containing liquids or gases. Such disks are inserts of metal weaker than the basic material of the vessel. In case of excessive pressure, the rupture disks break before the pressure becomes strong enough to explode the vessel.

of such compensations as delay, avoidance, inappropriate giving up, and slowing down among the exposed group." Also:
"Men with histories of multiple or severe exposure complain
directly and give evidence of being slowed down and less
energetic and of having increasing memory difficulty and greater
irritability than the minimally exposed group."

Neurological examinations were given to both highly exposed and minimally exposed workers. "There is no difference
between the groups in terms of such hard neurological signs
as sensory or motor deficits," the report says. "It is our impression that exposed men show more so-called 'soft' neurological signs such as minor coordination deficits and oculomotor
imbalance . . . slowness of thinking and calculation and
memory deficits."

The Metcalf-Holmes report says: "Electroencephalograms
have been done on all men in the current study. Men with
histories of organophosphorus (OP) exposure do not show the
typical minimal changes we have found among individuals
with chronic chlorinated hydrocarbon (CH) exposure. Chronic
CH exposure tends to lead to EEGs that are low-voltage, fast,
and poorly organized, with group trends toward a higher-
than-expected incidence of minor abnormalities. The OP
group exhibits contrast by virtue of higher voltage EEGs, with
more adequate and distinct maintenance of the normal alpha
rhythms."

Dr. Metcalf and his colleagues would like to continue their
study; they are searching for the money to do so. The men
who work in the insecticide plant would like to see it continued, for they would like to know where they stand. They
have been told little about the findings, probably because the
limited knowledge thus far gained would do more to disturb
them than to help them.

But they already are disturbed. They speak with agitation
of the undue number of divorces in their ranks. Yet they can
put their fingers on nothing. They have no confidence in the

company doctors, their impression being that the company doctors are concerned only in extreme cases.

Eckenroth tells of one such case: "This fellow got an overexposure of phosdrin (an organophosphorus insecticide.) They had to put him in a straitjacket and ran him to the hospital." Shortly after this, the young man got his draft call, but was rejected by the armed forces because of this exposure to phosdrin. He was working toward a commercial pilot's license and almost lost it.

Such dramatic cases are few in number, but it is understandable that men who are subjected to lesser exposures of highly concentrated insecticides five days per week cry out for medical research, as do those who breathe toxic fumes and inhale noxious dust in other branches of industry.

6

Who Did It?

Finding the answers about possible brain and nerve damage which may be caused by exposures to insecticides will require intensive research over a long period of time. Shell employees think, however, that more mundane problems such as rashes on buttocks can be eliminated by very simple precautions.

Shell management refuses, in negotiations with the union, to write health and safety provisions into the labor-management contract at the Denver insecticide plant. It refuses to recognize a union safety committee even for purposes of discussion of problems. The alternative left to the workers is informal complaining to supervisors and more formal protests voiced by the regular union grievance committee. Nothing in the union contract obliges the company to listen to the protests, but the union lodges them anyway.

For a long time, the committee petitioned management to install toilets near the operating units, the nearest such facilities being some distance away in locker rooms. Eventually the company did so, shielding them by nothing more than enclosures with open tops, very near toxification units—one of them within about five feet. A toxification unit is where the most deadly components of the particular insecticide are injected into the mixture. The men say that toxic materials frequently escape and settle on the toilet seats, forming an oily scum. The men are reluctant to sit on the polluted stools, and when they do, they sometimes get skin rashes as a result.

After further protests from the men, the company provided

paper protective covers such as are sometimes found in public restrooms. In exasperation, union officers complained to the Colorado Industrial Commission. This institution, following the time-honored practice of most state regulatory agencies, apparently checked with the company—perhaps even inspected the place—but never contacted the union spokesmen so they could point out the hazardous situation.

Perhaps as a result of the complaint to the state agency, another great leap forward was made. "Blue Magic"—the little drip-drip of a blue-colored so-called disinfectant—or is it just a deodorant?—was added to the toilet water. "We have blue pools now," says Dick Eckenroth bitterly.

Means of correcting, or at least substantially mitigating, the rash-causing toilet situation are obvious and simple—and not very expensive. The toilet stalls could be completely enclosed. Air could be pumped into tightly enclosed booths so that positive pressure would be maintained, thus effectively preventing the poisoned air from coming in.

There's no place in the Shell plant to get away from trouble. Some years back several men quit their jobs in the Acedrin manufacturing unit and bumped back into the labor gang to get away from the stuff. Some employees think this is why the company eliminated the labor gang—to close one of the escape routes for the men. "When you're exposed to Acedrin," says Eckenroth, "your muscles start tightening up, you get the jumps, your eyes pinpoint, you get diarrhea."

The men complain about inadequate ventilation in the buildings. They have petitioned the State Industrial Commission for help, thus far to no avail, and they've been promised relief by the company. "The company keeps telling us they're going to improve it and they don't," says Eckenroth.

The plant has a dieldrin flaker, which creates a considerable amount of dust. (A flaker is a device for drying liquids into flakes, or small solid particles.) The ventilation system picks this up and it goes through a tunnel underground and out to a series of ducts outside the building. Then a blower fan blows it vertically through a stack up about 20 feet. About 15 feet away from the opening of that stack is the suction for the ventilation for the lunchroom in Building 514. When employees raised an objection about this, the company put a carbon filter in it, but apparently those filters are seldom changed. The air horn (which brings ventilation air into the lunchroom) is located above the lunch table and there is a considerable accumulation of dust around it which likely is quite high in dieldrin, it was reported by employees in February, 1970.

In the research project conducted among these workers by Dr. Metcalf, concentrations of dieldrin were found in fat biopsies taken from the men. It has not been indicated whether the concentrations were at dangerous levels. But what is a dangerous level? Dieldrin is a chlorinated hydrocarbon, akin to DDT.

The list of exposures in the Shell plant continues. There are occasional breaks in chlorine lines. There is raw ammonia. Most of the gas masks provided for protection against the organic insecticides are ineffective against chlorine and ammonia. There are fuming acids—nitric and sulfuric. A form of pneumonitis develops on inhalation of the fumes from either sulfuric or nitric acid.

In an interview on February 27, 1970, Eckenroth and David Towler reported a leak that had prevailed for the preceding three weeks in a unit which is toxified with trimethyl phosphate to make Acedrin. "The company has been putting us off and putting us off because it would take almost two weeks to completely evacuate everything and clean it out and go in and repair it. So what they do is put us off and put us off," says Eckenroth. "Finally, they built a box around it and put an elephant trunk (a flexible duct pipe) over to the blower —the suction of the blower—to try to keep the fumes from coming into the area."

Men working in this unit have cholinesterase levels measured in their blood at three-week intervals. In the three-week period of the unrepaired leak, according to Towler, nine of the 12 men whose work takes them into the immediate vicinity showed drops in cholinesterase levels.

These comments made by the Shell employees have been presented at some length because they indicate management hesitance to face up to health problems, an attitude in sharp contrast with the representations made by industry spokesmen when they parade before Congressional committees to testify in opposition to industrial health and safety legislation.

J. Sharp Queener of DuPont Company, testifying before a House committee February 29, 1968 on behalf of the United States Chamber of Commerce, said, "We find that 80 to 90 percent of the injuries which are occurring in our company are due to a human failure rather than a piece of equipment, a machine, or so on." Raymond J. Lyons testified before the same committee five days later on behalf of the National Association of Manufacturers. He said, "The human factor is the most important cause of accidents and injuries. It has been estimated that 75 to 80 percent of all such occurrences have been caused by a negligent or unsafe act on the part of the individual. It is essential that positive safety attitudes and safety consciousness be instilled through proper training and educational programs."

Like nearly all management spokesmen, Queener and Lyons carefully alluded to *injuries* as contrasted to *health damage*. Careful examination of all testimony offered by management reveals an overwhelming silence on the subject of health, with the exception that Manufacturing Chemists Association has boasted of its Chemical Safety Data Sheets which set forth health hazards of 90-odd widely used chemicals.

Are the management spokesmen correct when they blame individual workmen for accidents? The Safety and Fire Protection Committee of Manufacturing Chemists Association has published two volumes entitled "Case Histories of Accidents in the Chemical Industry," the first in 1962, the second in 1966. These case histories are simply condensations of *reports turned into the Association by managers—presumably company safety directors.* They reflect the management view. Each accident reported is described and in most cases a cause is assigned and the resultant corrective action is reported.

A total of 992 accidents are reported. Of these, 402 resulted from faulty equipment—either wrongly designed equipment or badly maintained equipment. Faulty methods of operation, dictated by management, caused 356 of the accidents. These two *management-caused* shortcomings account for 758 of the 992 accidents. Simple human error was blamed in only 75 of the accidents, less than eight percent. Combined equipment flaws and human error caused 52, combined faulty procedures and human error accounted for 45, while 19 were attributed to inadequate training. The remaining 43 were difficult to classify.

Those imperious men who are always so eager to pass the buck downhill should bear in mind that human errors can be made by captains and kings as well as working men. John O. Logan, for example, might take a look at his own backyard. He appeared before House and Senate committees in 1968 to testify as chairman of the board of directors of Manufacturing Chemists Association. In fairness, it must be said that his opposition to Federal laws protecting workers was much milder than that of most industry spokesmen; mostly he was just hung up on the notion that the states, not the Federal government, should enforce health and safety standards.

Logan boasted, with some justification, of the Chemical Safety Data Sheets published by MCA. These are good, as far as they go. They are available for 30 cents each to all companies, but far too few copies are purchased by the companies. It is extremely rare that a copy is shown to a workman who has to handle the chemical in question.

Logan also is president of Universal Oil Products Company. One of the products handled in that company's Shreveport, Louisiana, plant is paranitroaniline, the poison referred to in Chapter 2. The Chemical Safety Data Sheet published by MCA on paranitroaniline says: "Housekeeping and general cleanliness is highly important in the storage and handling of PNA. Any dust from handling or breakage should be promptly washed down with water."

Says F. Q. Hood, local union secretary, of PNA conditions in Logan's Shreveport plant: "Of course we have a lot of it around on the floor. And of course this old dryer we got, we bought it second hand. I don't know how old it is and it leaks pretty badly. The dust comes out of it and gets on the floor. You get it on you and you track it. There's always some on the decks around."

The PNA data sheet says: "Contaminated shoes should be discarded and replaced." Hood says: "The company furnishes us one pair of shoes a year. We buy anything beyond that. The men usually use them a good while. They wear them out."

The data sheet includes approximately 350 words of recommendations on *education and training* of employees who are expected to handle paranitroaniline. Hood says, "I tried to get the company safety director to initiate some kind of safety program. I feel that all the people would like to work safe, but I feel you have to impress it on your people periodically and really bring it to their attention. I think it would be a good idea if they would go in there and gather up the men and have a little safety meeting. I brought it up with management, but management says we haven't got time to do this."

You don't have any safety meetings at all?

Hood: "No safety meetings at all. I've been there 19 years."

When a man is hired, does he get any safety training or does he just pick it up from the fellow above him?

Hood: "He picks up our bad habits, that's about all. I mean, they give him a face mask and a respirator and tell him to work safe. That's the extent of it." The lack of training of new employees is particularly worrisome to Hood because he thinks they do not have enough fear of the toxic materials. "The thing about it is that these boys they use in the cleanup crew are usually your youngest men. They're just coming

into the industry to work in their first job and they're not
oriented on safety too well. They're trying to do good work
to hold their jobs. They'll stay in there and fight that stuff.
Management tells them to, while some of the older hands like
me—well, they're not going to make me get in there."

Hood is concerned not only about paranitroaniline but also
about frequent exposures to chlorine, sulfuric acid, ammonia,
hydrochloric acid, chloroplatinic acid and other chemicals used
in the plant.

It is not to be denied that working people sometimes bring
their troubles on themselves. They can be awkward. They
can be careless. They can take shortcuts that are dangerous.
A man can remove protective rubber gloves just because he is
annoyed by the sweat they cause. Most companies have rules
providing for discipline or discharge of men who violate safety
rules, although in general these rules are neither uniformly
nor sternly enforced.

People naturally resent rules, even when the rules are for
their own good, just as many law-abiding citizens resent traffic laws and the policemen whose duty it is to enforce them.
Respect for rules, like respect for law, depends in large measure on the fairness of the rules and the even-handedness with
which they are enforced. If safety rules are clearly explained
and discussed with the men, greater respect is obtained. If
foremen themselves set good examples by meticulously following rules, a general attitude of respect for rules usually ensues.
But if rules are simply commandments posted on bulletin boards
or distributed in booklets with emphasis on the punitive
aspects, they tend to arouse resentment, as a motorcycle cop
behind a billboard arouses resentment. Regrettably, some
companies take this latter approach to safety rule making and
enforcement.

Working people, even more than people of greater economic accomplishment, are quite sensitive to real or imagined
affronts to personal dignity. This is a fact too often over-
looked. The man sentenced to a lifetime of routine work with

little or no authority over others and little or no prospect of advancement places great store on personal dignity. He doesn't like to be talked down to, but in most cases will extend himself to be cooperative if he is taken into partnership in a manner which reveals no condescension by the other party.

Effective application of health and safety rules calls for more than a simple enunciation. Required is explanation, discussion and participation. This is particularly true regarding complex health matters. A physical safety rule may be simple, such as "Always replace the safety guard over the drive belt before starting machine." But regarding a toxic chemical, it is not sufficient to say, "Be careful not to inhale fumes or get liquid on your skin." It is necessary to explain why and to clarify the degree of exposure that is tolerable. It is not sufficient to hang a gas mask on a peg and say, "Put this on if there is a leakage of gas." Instructions and rehearsals must be provided, and repeated intermittently for refresher purposes, on how to use the mask.

Speaking for the National Association of Manufacturers, Raymond J. Lyons says that "it is essential that positive safety attitudes and safety consciousness be instilled through proper training and educational programs," but most member companies of NAM do little or nothing in the area of training and education on safety. In some plants, no training at all is given. In others it is haphazard, irregular and devoted more to simple mechanical precautions than to the complex matters in which detailed education is necessary. In some cases, so-called safety training is a fraud, devoted more to discussion of production quotas or out-of-plant safety than to real involvement with work practices.

J. Sharp Queener, quoted earlier in this chapter as spokesman for the United States Chamber of Commerce, is employed by DuPont. He says 80 to 90 percent of the injuries in his company are due to human failure. Yet Johnny L. Cicero, union president in DuPont's Watson, Alabama, high explosives plant, testifies that new employees there are given no formal

safety training. Asked if he thought most of the men in the
plant are reasonably cautious, Cicero says, "I'd say the majority
of men are, your older men are. At the present we have a lot
of young employees that it will take years to teach safety."

Question: When a new man is hired, is he given formal
training in avoiding hazards?

Cicero: "This is where the company is really lax in our
location. They bring a new employee in and they turn him
loose, you might say. It's going to take him a long time, I would
say years, to become a safe worker."

No doubt a veteran employee can provide a new employee
more practical training in safety than could be extended by a
reasonably thorough but necessarily brief formal training period
—if the new man is assigned in such way that he is under
constant surveillance by the experienced man. This is not
always the case; in industry new employees often are assigned
to floating labor gangs not closely supervised.

Cicero also states that DuPont does not give the employees
literature providing detail on possible hazards and the cautions
to be followed in handling chemicals. DuPont does conduct
regular safety meetings of all employees, by departments. But
Cicero says health matters, possible hazards of such chemicals
as glycol, and that sort of thing are never discussed. The safety
training is limited to avoidance of immediate physical accidents.

In the Union Carbide (Linde Division) plant at Tonawanda, New York, there are implications that instructions are
lacking in some important physical precautions. Ray Stahley,
a calm, mature craftsman of the old school, says that he was
assigned to operate a crane without training (he is a welder).
"I was not given any instructions," he says. "About a year and
a half ago, my foreman, Raymond Buckner, approached me
and asked me if I knew where the crane shut-off switches were
in case of emergency. I told him I didn't and he showed me
where they were. And I said they should be painted a different
color so we don't have to go looking for them. He agreed with

me. It was only last week they finally put up signs, green and white, showing where the crane switches are."

Don Kreuter of the same plant says new chemical operators are given mathematics tests to determine if they are competent to calculate how many gallons an hour a given pump will move, but they are not given breakdowns of the chemicals they are going to handle. They are not told the hazards.

Suppose a young man, new on the job, gets a caustic spill on him. How does he know to go jump under the safety shower?

Kreuter: "By the old-timers there going and shoving him under the shower."

An accident described in a previous chapter killed three men and injured 14 in the American Oil Refinery at Texas City, Texas. All were victims of hydrogen sulfide gas. "Some of the people who came to try to effect a rescue and were injured were totally unfamiliar with the Scott Air Pak equipment," says Local President Leo Reidel. "It operates on a demand system, that is, the air doesn't flow to you until you breathe; either that or there is a valve you turn on to give a continuous flow, but that doesn't give you very much air. Not knowing this, some of the people using the masks were afraid they would suffocate. They opened the sides of their masks and got enough gas to knock them out."

Insufficient masks were available in the immediate vicinity of the accident and the tool room was not open for issuance of additional masks. One of the workers got in a truck and rushed around to various other sections of the plant borrowing masks for use in the emergency. Since that accident, American Oil has increased the supply of masks convenient to each unit and has conducted refresher training in their use.

In the American Cyanamid plant in Kalamazoo, Michigan, several toxic chemicals are handled. How do the men learn about them? Harry Miller, chief union steward, says new employees are not given instructions and precautions about these chemicals, but pick up their information gradually from older employees.

Stories of lack of training are repeated in plant after plant. But what may be worse than no training at all is unrealistically directed training. Safety sessions devoted in large part to outside-of-plant hazards are offensive; it is insulting to the average man to be lectured by management about his conduct off the company premises. Asked what is discussed in safety meetings in the Reactive Metals, Incorporated, metals reduction plant at Ashtabula, Ohio, Charles Moore replies bitterly, "Don't put your feet under the lawnmower." Moore is a dignified, middle-aged man who undoubtedly has mowed many a lawn, as well as worked for decades with complex industrial machinery.

Lawrence Scafuro, local union president, adds, "They maybe talk about safety at home, safety on vacation. In the plant, maybe the proper use of tools. We do have pictures of proper driving of tow motors, proper use of grinding tools. The foreman will ask employee suggestions for safety. Now, I'm talking about the maintenance department. I don't know about the production department."

Charles Valerio, safety chairman in the production department, responds: "Up until six months ago the safety meeting went like this: 'This is fire prevention week.' It's all over fire prevention. 'Now our quota for this month is so many thousand pounds. Our quality is down and some of you guys are not doing the work. The meeting is over.' " Valerio adds that in recent months the meetings have been extended to an average of 20 minutes, including arguments between the men and supervision. "We bring up a safety suggestion and nothing is done about it. You don't even hear an answer as to why it was done or wasn't done."

In management's long chain of command from foreman to department supervisor to plant superintendent and on up to corporate headquarters, there is much room for misunderstanding, lack of cooperation—and outright falsification of reports.

All high-ranking officials know, or should know, that short-comings down the line sometimes are hidden behind smoothly maintained but deceptive records.

An extreme and no doubt unusual case of falsification on safety matters shows up in the Stauffer Chemical Company plant in Chicago Heights. Let Fred Mayfield, an employee, tell the story: "I don't know what the gimmick is, whether it's the bonus or what, but each foreman goes along with a green safety card in his pocket. He is supposed to contact the employee and when he does, as far as I can see, he only contacts him to get his name written on this card. He will say, for example, 'I'm supposed to talk to you today on hard hats,' or something of that nature. 'Sign your name.' Well, he's got your name and gone. He hasn't said anything. Just wanted to get your name. I suppose they have to turn in this card each month."

Opal Swafford of the same plant adds, "He says, 'This is a safety meeting. Sign this card.' I say, 'Well, what's it all about?' He says, 'Well, hard hats, glasses, anything you want to think about.' You sign it and that's about all the conversation you get." Francisco Montalvo, local union president, comments: "The foremen, most of them, will just come to you and say, 'Here, sign this card for me.' The first thing I say is, 'You're supposed to tell me something about safety before I sign it.' So he'll say, 'Well, you go on vacation in the summer. Make sure you don't get hurt,' or 'Drive carefully and come back.' " Mayfield adds that one time he demurred when a foreman asked for his signature without actually discussing safety. For this he got a verbal reprimand.

Lack of training can be a matter of concern for people outside the industrial plants as well as those inside. Huge trucks carrying highly explosive petroleum products, strong acids and dangerous poisons run over public roads and streets. Public safety is in the hands of the skilled men who drive those trucks.

Many companies issue shoulder or breast insignia a driver

can sew on his shirt if he has a long accident-free record. "They're real proud when they've got an 18- or 20-year patch," says J. Roy Johnston, president of a Detroit local representing tanker truck drivers. "That says 20 years' safe driving. The public sees that when you get out of your truck. But most companies don't have any safety meetings," continues Johnston. "The man driving that kind of equipment, to operate in a metropolitan area like Detroit, is very lucky when he can get, say, three years' safe driving, let alone 18 or 20. We do have people with 25 years' safe driving."

Johnston recalls that in earlier years there were regular safety training sessions. "They'd call the day drivers in in the morning and also they'd have a meeting at night for night men. They'd have coffee and doughnuts and the safety director, or maybe just the top boss, would be there explaining safety and things that happen. Also, then, we'd have an old truck that was out of commission. They'd put old tires on it and fill it with some gas and they'd practice what should be done in case of fire. They'd have each one of the drivers approach this truck to see what he would do if a fire happened to him. But this has been discontinued. Very seldom do they have this type of meeting anymore because it's dog-eat-dog and they're trying to save money. You can't be in a meeting and producing for the company at the same time."

Johnston reports with concern that one employer requires his drivers to move a 42-wheel rig out of the yard within five minutes of reporting to work. "Ray Molner, owner of Molner Transportation and president of Refiners Transport, demands that the driver take that truck and check it in five minutes. You can't check a truck in five minutes," protests Johnston.

What does a driver have to do to safety check a truck?

Johnston: "First of all, he has to build up the air; he's got to have 50 to 100 pounds of pressure. Then he's got to check the air brakes by putting them on and going to see if his stop lights are working on the back unit and the front unit. Then he has to go back and release the brakes and turn on the lights and get out and check the lights. He's got to check all the tires. He's got to kick the inside duals. He can tell pretty near just by touching the outside tires, but he has to get where he can put his foot in and kick the inside tires. He's got 20 inside wheels to kick. It's against the law to drive one of these flammable liquid trucks with a flat tire because it can create a fire. Then, you've got to know for sure that you have air hose connections between the two units, that nobody's touched it or that the unit hasn't been taken apart to be backed inside somewhere and the air not re-connected."

In this and other safety considerations, the wage-earning man finds himself under intolerable pressures. He can, of course, simply refuse to work when he thinks the assignment is too dangerous. Sometimes this happens. But in few cases is he protected against discharge if he refuses to accept a work order. It becomes a matter of a man balancing his safety against his semi-monthly paycheck. Deeply convinced that an assignment seriously endangers his life, a man likely will risk losing his job. The more typical problem involves a marginal situation that may, just may, be dangerous, just as it may be dangerous to drive an automobile at an excessive rate of speed. In borderline danger situations, desire to preserve the paycheck often overcomes caution.

This is especially true in dealing with the relatively unknown effects of toxic materials. J. W. Carpenter, local union president representing workers in the big Geigy Chemical Company insecticide plant at McIntosh, Alabama, explains the marginal situation this way: "We're working in things that we don't know how they affect us. Herbicides, insecticides, things of this nature. The people who are formulating this are just in a dust bed. They will give you a little paper mask to put over your mouth and your nose, but this is not sufficient."

The men in that plant also have problems with fumes, including those of chlorine. Asked what the company response is when the union complains about health hazards, Carpenter says, "Well, you can go to the company about so-and-so working

in fumes that are unbearable. Their standard answer is, 'When
the fumes get too bad, get out.' Well, this is not sufficient
answer. Anyway, three minutes later a supervisor comes by
and says, 'It is cleared up now, you can go back in.' So you
go on back in and then you come back out. What are you
accomplishing when you do this?" Carpenter lists chlorine
fumes, cyanuric chloride fumes and others troublesome where
he works. Cyanuric chloride is a compound of chlorine and
hydrogen cyanide, a quick and deadly chemical. Carpenter
recalls that Edward Patrick was overcome by hydrogen cyanide.
"One night he got hydrogen cyanide to the extent that he just
completely passed out, quit breathing, turned black around his
mouth, his nose, his fingernails. He was a big, husky, healthy,
normal guy. So after this he kept complaining of a headache.
Eventually he quit Geigy and got another job and then died of
some cause unknown to me."

Not the slightest evidence has been developed that Edward Patrick's death, after leaving Geigy, was attributable
to the work environment at Geigy. There is no hard evidence
that Patrick's close shave with death while on the job at Geigy
can be attributed to bad operating procedures in the plant,
although the burden of suspicion weighs heavily on a management which permits toxic fumes to prevail in the work place.

But under most present managerial systems in America, the
responsibility must be borne by management. This is because
management of nearly every company has demanded that it
retain what it calls "management rights"—the responsibility for
directing the work force and for "running" the plant. This
demand comes from a generally prevailing attitude that is
something of an article of faith in managerial circles, an attitude based on the fundamental conflict between unions and
employers.

In the absence of unions, employers could totally dictate
all terms and conditions to employees. Their power would be
absolute. But this power has been diluted since the development of collective bargaining. First, workers organized into

the union for the primary purpose of negotiating rates of pay and limits to the hours of work. This, in most cases, was all they could hope for. An exception may be noted in the early railroad labor organizations, where the train crewmen and switchmen also were deeply concerned by the then massive number of accidents which killed or maimed hundreds of men each year.

Gradually, the scope of union negotiating efforts broadened. Unions now negotiate not only on rates of pay and hours of work, but also on overtime pay, numerous fringe benefits such as pensions and medical insurance plans, holidays, vacations, job security and availability of soap in the wash rooms. That labor should negotiate on all these things is logical since each represents a condition of work which is to one degree or another meaningful, just as the basic rate of pay is meaningful. The scope of union-management bargaining is summed up in the basic labor laws of the United States, Canada and the various states and provinces which guarantee the rights of workers to organize and to negotiate on wages, hours *and conditions of work.* The result is that the typical union contract is as long as perhaps 40 or 50 pages of this book, whereas a simple listing of wage scales might fill one page.

Each time a union negotiates in a new field and adds a new contract provision limiting management's unlimited and arbitrary control of the work place, the power of management is eroded. Frustrated by this trend, owners of small companies have been known to toss their keys on the bargaining table and angrily declare, "Here, you guys run this plant—you don't want to allow me to do it." To be sure, it is doubtful if there has ever been a case when such an owner failed to retrieve his keys after a few minutes; the profit incentive overcomes frustrations. At a more formal level, employers generally insist on writing into each contract a "management rights" clause which sets forth those things the management can do totally without restriction by union or individual workers.

These management rights clauses vary in strength and

scope. The Allied Chemical Corporation contract with Oil, Chemical and Atomic Workers at Ironton, Ohio, specifies that management rights include, but are not limited to, "(1) full and exclusive control of the management and operation of the plant; (2) the direction and supervision of the working forces; (3) the right to determine the extent to which, and the means and manner by which, the plant and the various departments thereof shall be operated and shut down; (4) reduction or increase of working forces or production; (5) the right to modify, change or eliminate any jobs or classifications and create new jobs or classifications; (6) the right to introduce new or improved production methods or facilities x x x."

The Wyandotte Chemicals Corporation contract at Wyandotte, Michigan, gives management the clear right "to determine production schedules, methods of operation, character of work to be done and the assignment thereof." Contract after contract provides that the management may "prescribe the work to be performed."

With exceptions so rare as to be insignificant, unions recognize the employers' rights to control production. If a man is assigned at $3.87 per hour plus stated fringe benefits to operate a given machine, it fundamentally is none of his concern whether that machine is producing widgets or gadgets. The union position is that it has a right, however, to negotiate on anything that affects the individual laborer's *working conditions.*

Such phrases as "prescribe the work to be performed" may impinge on the individual's working conditions. This phrase may be construed to give management the right to order a man to overload a production facility in such way as to create a hazard, or to order a man to enter a storage tank or a building where conditions may be dangerous to health.

Most managers intend to exercise their rights "to prescribe the work to be performed" in sensible ways. Few get belligerent about it, as did Gregory Tobin, a labor relations official from the head office of Carborundum Company when he was in negotiations with the union committee of the company's Hickman, Kentucky, plant in 1969. He insisted that management should have an unlimited right to order men around. President Henry Callison of the local union said, "You mean to tell me that if you told me to get on one of those silos out there, 50 to 80 feet high, and jump, I would have to jump?" According to Callison, Tobin replied that this would, indeed, be the rule although of course no such situation likely would come up.

To counter this sort of threat—or, more pertinently, the threat of being assigned to marginally unsafe work—unions often ask for contract clauses giving the individual workman the right to refuse to do any job he considers unsafe. A very few contracts give workers this right. These can lead to complicated litigation. The man's refusal can be unreasonable or capricious; in such case, management may wish to protest the refusal and punish the workman by an action such as a disciplinary layoff of a few days' duration. The union tends to protect the workman and the result may be argument of the case before an impartial arbitrator, who hears the evidence on both sides and makes a final judgment as to whether or not the man had reasonable grounds to refuse to perform the work.

Numerous contracts provide for establishment of joint union-management safety committees to *discuss* health and safety conditions. Such a committee typically consists of three members designated by the union and three designated by management from supervisory ranks. These committees in some cases—far too few cases—accomplish practical improvements in health and safety conditions. But final decisions always are made solely by management. The union spokesmen may propose changes, but management retains full authority. Still other contracts provide no mention of health and safety; many companies insist that it is management's sole prerogative to make decisions in this area.

In summary, management in nearly all plants refuses to accept union partnership in improving health and safety conditions. Therefore, when blood is spilled, the blood is on management hands. Unless and until management shares responsibility with the unions and/or with government regulatory agencies, management must shoulder the blame for the accidents and illnesses of the work place.

7

The Dollar Yardstick

Bob Walter, a union leader in the Rohm & Haas Chemical Company plant near Pasadena, Texas, is a relaxed sort of man who is generally complimentary about the precautions taken by management in the handling of the extraordinarily toxic chemicals processed there. But he's concerned about leakages of hydrogen cyanide, the gas used in execution chambers and many industrial chemical formulations.

Walter and his fellow workers are better informed than are most industrial workers about the chemical properties of the materials they work with. They understand hydrogen cyanide, respect it, and speak of it almost casually.

"We have fresh air masks in all the cells for people who have to go in where there's any concentration of gas," Walter points out. "Normally a man isn't permitted to go into a cell alone; somebody has to stand by watching him. That's because we have had several incidents where men were overcome with HCN and people have had to rush in and pull them out and revive them with oxygen."

How often have men been overcome?

Walter: "Well, this is a varying thing. It's under high pressure and it varies depending on the number of leaks that turn up in a unit. We've had a lot of problems here recently getting maintenance work done on the leaks in the hydrogen cyanide department."

You put in requests for repairs and you say you have difficulties getting them done?

Walter: "Oh, yes. Well, I'm sure they are just like any other chemical plant. They hate to shut down to fix anything. They'll let it run as long as they possibly can before they'll shut it down to repair it. Anytime you go into the cyanide units, you can go report it to the foreman and on a lot of occasions the foreman will say, 'Oh, it's not that bad, you go ahead on in there.'" On occasion Walter has refused to go into the units, on the grounds of safety, but he has not been disciplined for this.

In his mild-mannered criticism of company failure to repair leaks promptly, Walter is touching on what is perhaps the most universal complaint voiced by industrial workers. Most are much more vehement than Walter.

"The maintenance in this plant stinks," says Bob Palmer of the Witco Chemical plant in Perth Amboy, New Jersey. "They got lines leaking all over the joint. I can give you one example, a caustic line. Now I don't know how long it was leaking, but every pumper reported that line for repair and they never did anything about it until just recently. We had this guy here that actually the paint on his helmet and his jacket got eaten up. See, he didn't know it was leaking, it was such a fine mist. He thought it was water. He went to wipe off his helmet and the paint came off on his glove."

Standing near the entry gate of his plant shortly after leaving work, Palmer adds: "In fact, on the unit I just left the bottom fell out of one reactor, the insulation fell out of it. They're shoring it up. Now the bottom is coming out, the insulation is letting go, yet they are going to run this kettle. They're going to shore it up and run it."

Will the shoring hold?

Palmer: "God damn better hold! Somebody's going to get killed if it don't. You're gonna knock out the power and everything."

The breakdown of the reactor occurred on a night shift. Palmer said a plant official had been telephoned at his home and alerted. The official did not come to the plant and inspect the situation; he simply advised the men to shore up the insulation and continue operating the damaged equipment.

While the above conversation with Palmer was taking place, a husky, clean-cut man in his twenties, on duty as gateman, pointedly moved out of earshot. It seemed curious that a man in such prime condition would be holding the sedentary job of gatekeeper. The explanation came about incidentally. As the author started to leave, the young man—John Hollywood—extended a deformed right hand to shake. In response to an inquiring glance, he explained: "I get too hot when someone talks about safety." His hand had been mangled in an accident in the plant. Hollywood had been repairing a piece of machinery when someone inadvertently turned it on. A hundred dollar lockout device would have prevented his injury. Now men in that plant reportedly carry padlocks in their tool kits so that they can jerry-rig their own lockout systems when they repair machines. (A lockout device is an arrangement whereby a mechanic may positively lock a machine in an inoperable condition while he is working on it).

The saving of a hundred dollars, or a hundred dollars multiplied by the number of machines in a plant, is a budget item of some concern to a plant manager. He is allowed a certain amount of money each year for regular maintenance. If he holds expenditures under this figure, his record looks good to the corporate vice president for manufacturing. If he has to petition for more money, he has explaining to do. If he needs to install entirely new equipment to correct a hazardous situation, it likely is necessary to ask the home office for a separate appropriation, and the home office is a long way, environmentally, from the stinking plant.

Fumes from sulfuric acid, ammonia and other chemicals, along with dust, constantly plague employees of Farmers Chemical Company in Joplin, Missouri. Leo Simonds, local union president, has discussed the problem with management. "They come out with a budget every year," he says, "and they try to stay in the limits of this budget, and usually this budget

doesn't allow for too much of their funds to go for improving
the ventilation system and fans." Simonds has the impression
that the manager of this multi-million dollar plant cannot spend
more than $200 on any project without obtaining approval
of the home office in Kansas City.

New projects aside, maintenance of existing equipment
often is carried out pretty much on a make-do basis. Wayne
Hood of the same Farmers Chemical plant says, "I work
in maintenance and the procedure out there is just patch it
and go on, just patch it so they can get back into operation as
quickly as possible. There are lots of places where they may
just put a piece of rubber on a leak and tape it down and of
course there's still seepage. It's not repaired, it's just patched,
and there are still fumes that can get out around this."

Some companies make greater efforts than others, but the
budget bugaboo always seems to remain. According to Bill
Higgins, local union president in the Reichhold Chemical
plant in Elizabeth, New Jersey, that company is quite conscientious about safety. The union safety committee regularly
calls to management's attention any unsafe conditions. "Their
reactions are good," Higgins says of his managers. "We have
no complaint when it's immediate, if there's anything they can
do, providing it's within the budget that they're allowed to
work with. But if it goes into big money items, it has to go
through the main office in White Plains and this is a stumbling
block. I think this is not unusual."

He gives as an example a request that a second stairway
or escape chute be built on a five-story high distillation unit
turning out phthalic anhydride. As it is, there is only one
stair and in case of fire men on upper levels might be trapped.
The local manager has endorsed building a second stairway,
but money has not been appropriated by the home office.

The reluctance of Glascote Products Division, Haveg Industries, to spend money for ventilation devices in its Cleveland
plant causes the 225 men there to work in almost constantly
miserable conditions. This shop manufactures glass-lined steel

vessels used as reactors, mixing vessels and storage tanks for various chemical processes. Every step of the process produces either fumes or dust. Plates of steel are fabricated into vessels and welded—with fumes resulting. Men using abrasive tools grind down the welds inside the vessels. Then the inside is sandblasted to provide a smooth, clean surface. Next, finely ground glass mixed with liquid binders is sprayed over the inside surfaces. The tank goes into a furnace to fuse this coating to the steel. After it is cooled, a man goes inside with an abrasive wheel and grinds it down. Where necessary, imperfect spots are spotblasted or gritblasted. Finally, a second coat of glass is sprayed over the inside of the tank.

The company provides various portable ventilation devices to draw fumes, the sand from spotblasting or grinding and dusts from inside the tanks. But instead of these being exhausted from the building, they are just pumped out into the shop where other employees can breathe them, along with fumes from the welding operations.

Vice President George Shiner of the local union says, "There is no receiving area for this polluted air. It is simply re-circulating in the same atmosphere in which other employees are working with no respirators." The men have asked for better ventilation. "We have begged them, but nobody seems to want to do anything about it," says LeRoy Hale, local union secretary. "We have tried to get management to put more ventilation over in the glassing area to keep the dust, this over-spray and stuff, going outside instead of coming over there on our side of the shop." The Glascote plant consists of an old building approximately 100 by 400 feet in dimension and an addition of about 300 by 60 feet built in 1965. Even in the new building, management cut corners by not installing adequate ventilation.

The men in the General American Transportation Company terminal in Carteret, New Jersey, complain of constant and persistent leaks of many of the approximately 100 different chemicals they handle. "Some of these leaks are maybe two or three years old," says Rich Wadiak of that plant. "The only way we can get them fixed is if we constantly harp on these people and tell them the customer's products are being lost. But it takes them so doggone long to get it fixed and meantime this is all contaminating the ground." Emil Peter adds, "In our transfer (of products from tank trucks, railway tank cars and barges to and from storage tanks) we use a lot of hose and many of the hoses we're using now are just rotten." Local President Jim Irving says, "One of the biggest cries we hear from our company is that 'we have not appropriated money for this year to take care of some of the safety problems and we cannot do anything until we make such appropriations'." And the years go by without those appropriations ever coming around.

A matter of somewhat over $2,500 has delayed the installation of a needed safety device in the Wyandotte Chemical plant at Baton Rouge, Louisiana. A fire occurred on a structure in the boiler area which is five platforms high—more than a hundred feet. Fortunately, no workmen were on the structure at the time. But Andy Wise, an employee, complained that if a man had been on the fifth level, he very well could have been trapped because there is only one ladder down. He asked for some kind of alternate escape route—even a glide bar a man could grab and slide down.

The company agreed to install a second ladder. Eighteen months passed before action was taken, then a walkway was installed, but only to the third platform. Wise called supervision and said, "Look, you're putting this in the wrong place." The supervisor said, "Well, that's the engineers; they've made a mistake." But Wise reminded supervision that they had shown him a letter of bid from a contractor to build the second ladder and that the letter specified a ladder to the fifth level.

"It ran over $2,500 and they had to wait to the end of the year to appropriate the money," explains Wise. After more complaints from Wise, the company extended the ladder to the fifth level, more than a year and a half after agreeing that it was needed.

In the Wyandotte facility, routine repairs leave much to be desired. Chlorine fumes are rather constant around the plant, a major producer of this gas. Don Courtney, union committeeman, believes that these could be reduced or virtually eliminated by more frequent replacement of "headers" over the cells which liberate chlorine from brine by electrolysis. The header is a long fiberglass pipe into which the newly formed chlorine is sucked for pumping into the drying process and on to storage vessels. In time, it becomes worn and leaky around connections.

Courtney has repeatedly asked the company to replace leaking headers. According to Courtney, management's reaction is, "We're going to do it. We know that they're bad and we're going to do it, but we're going to have to shut down to do it. We've got to shut down next month." And next month never seems to get here. "For instance, our shutdown now has been put off since sometime last July or August." (He was speaking in January). "We shut down on an emergency basis for about 24 hours one time. We didn't exchange headers then because we had other things to do." Some headers have been unchanged for as long as 10 years.

Leaks occur in pipes carrying chemicals through the Wyandotte plant. Asked what kind of repairs were made, Courtney says, "Band aid, if you know what the industry calls a band aid. It's a worm drive clamp with a rubber stopper. You put it over the hole and turn the worm drive and just tighten it down. We use epoxy glue—smear it on the hole and tape it. We put vinyl tape on it." This plant handles such chemicals as phosgene gas, methanes, glycol, toluene diisocyanate and toluene diamine, but chlorine brings about the most complaints. "We've had people—I think most of our people—including myself, go home afternoons after work suffering from tight chest and coughing and not being able to relax and having dizziness," says Courtney. "Sometimes I feel like I am a hazard to drive home."

The fallibility of design engineers who should have a concern for health and safety is reflected by Courtney in a comment about emergency fresh air supplied to air masks through hoses from a central compressed air source: "We've had problems with our air supply in that one time we had a leak of chlorine near the intake of the compressor that's used to pump the air. The compressor took chlorine and pumped it into the air line. Some of our people were overcome with gas through the fresh air line."

In nearly all chemical plants, the workmen complain of equipment leaks which expose them to toxic materials. An example is the Great Lakes Chemical facility in El Dorado, Arkansas, which extracts bromine from brine and then manufactures various derivatives and compounds based on bromine. Also involved is hydrogen sulfide gas, which comes out of the brine wells in this particular vicinity. In several forms, bromine derivatives are nerve poisons. There have been many serious illnesses among the work force as a result of exposures.

Wayne Jeter of this plant says, "We are exposed to fumes every day in the methyl bromide packing and shipping area." John Kennedy says that at least one time during the production of each batch of methyl bromide—a batch is produced each 10 hours—there will be leakage, generally around packing glands. Methyl bromide, used as an insecticide, irritates the lungs and damages the central nervous system. Non-fatal exposures may cause fatigue, double or blurred vision, nausea, incoordination, tremors and convulsions. For some reason, this company has not designed equipment which will contain its poisonous products without leaks. Such equipment can be designed.

The situation became so bad, the illnesses became so prevalent among this group of workmen, that the plant manager in 1969 called a meeting of all employees, members of their families and others in an auditorium in the downtown section of El Dorado. He promised that drastic revisions would be made. Some construction work started, then stopped abruptly. Suddenly the plant manager resigned and left the area on short notice. Many people in El Dorado believe that this manager resigned his job because he had been thwarted by higher company officials in his efforts to clean up the situation.

Maintenance of equipment takes four basic forms. There is emergency repair when something breaks down and will not operate. There is "running maintenance"—the making of minor repairs and adjustments on equipment while it is in operation. Then there is "major maintenance," which involves considerable planning and the dedication of much resources. It almost always is done during a total shutdown. Finally, there is, or should be, "preventive maintenance." This might be compared to the periodic examination, adjustment and lubrication recommended to automobile owners—a procedure calculated to forestall breakdowns.

Preventive maintenance of industrial equipment means repairing equipment before it malfunctions. Another name for this is "anticipatory maintenance." For example, a pipe or vessel showing extensive corrosion or revealing thin spots upon X-ray examination is replaced *before* it springs a leak. Complex equipment is taken out of operation periodically, taken apart, examined, and reassembled with worn or weakened parts replaced. Frequently, repairs are made simply because experience shows that failure will occur in "X" number of months and to forestall failure the repair is made in X minus Y months. Industrial workers are great proponents of preventive maintenance. They feel more secure working around equipment they know has been inspected and, if necessary, repaired fairly recently, just as a driver feels more secure when he knows that his car has good brakes, good wheel alignment and four good tires on the ground.

In the last 15 years, many companies have reduced preventive maintenance in order to save money. Continuous-flow refinery distillation units and chemical distillation or reactor units—these are facilities which operate non-stop, 24 hours per day, seven days per week—which in earlier years might have been taken out of operation once each year for overhaul, now may run two or three years non-stop. The financial incentives to management are great, for the costs of shutdown compound in three ways. There is the actual cost of labor and materials involved in examination and repair. There is the loss of profitable production during the shutdown period. And there is a domino effect from shutting down one unit: a long sequence of other operations dependent on the unit under repair also may have to cease operation. Complex refineries and chemical plants cannot be taken out of operation simply by throwing a switch. A period of three or four days may be required to take such a facility "off stream"—out of operation—and a similar period is needed to put it back "on stream."

Management contends that longer running periods are more acceptable now than in earlier times because equipment is better designed and made of stronger and more durable materials. Workers concede that this may be true up to a point, but they hold that management places too much trust in the new equipment. They think that bigness and complexity are the real causes of long non-stop runs.

As a matter of fact, some design engineers say that much modern equipment is more fragile than older types. Modern equipment is complex, operates at extremes of temperatures and pressures unheard of even a few years ago, and is very costly. In order to pare costs to the greatest extent, engineers design equipment as "close" as possible. In doing so, much of the margin of safety is eliminated.

A plant that 10 years ago might have had half a dozen identical distillation units or reactors performing the same process today may have one massive unit doing the same job— more efficiently and more profitably. When there were six separate units, they could be taken out of operation one at a time and repaired. Today, such overhaul means halting all production of the material handled by the one large unit.

L. E. Sanford of the Shell Oil refinery at Pasadena, Texas,

says, "I don't think there's any doubt but what the maintenance is worse now than it was 10 years ago." In the Shell Chemical plant extension of the oil refinery, a frightening accident occurred in January, 1968. A pipe carrying sulfuric acid and propylene under pressure of 450 pounds per square inch ruptured and a fire resulted. Fortunately, the blast was toward an open area; if the pipe had broken on the opposite side, fire and sulfuric acid would have shot into a complex of chemical process units. The pipe was found to have eroded to the point that its walls were as thin as the metal in a beer can.

President Roy Barnes of the local representing employees of these two Shell plants says, "It's quite obvious that maintenance has gone by the wayside. They maintain the plants only as necessary to keep them running. If they can keep it running, they do so until it falls apart." Barnes adds that some leaks are repaired with glass cloth and epoxy glue, a not at all uncommon technique in the industry.

An accident occurred in the Mobil refinery in East Chicago, Indiana, on January 17, 1970, which has suspicious similarities to the above-described pipe rupture in the Shell Chemical plant. A pipe carrying oil into the reduced crude furnace of the thermal catalytic cracking unit of the plant under 250 pounds per square inch pressure and 700 to 800 degrees temperature ruptured. Photos taken of a section of the tube showed it to be thin and badly corroded. Fortunately, no one was injured in the resulting fire, but a gas plant explosion in the same plant just five weeks earlier killed Boyd Hipsley.

The management desire to maintain non-stop production means that many "running repairs" are made under hazardous circumstances. Othel D. Newby, union chairman in the Atlantic Richfield refinery near Houston, says, "The main problem is that the oil companies have gone away from the methods we used to use. It used to be that when we worked [overhauled] a unit the whole unit was shut down. Now you have a little section you are working on down, but right by another section that's live. That can be very dangerous with crafts working all over on the high towers. If a man drops a piece of material or a wrench, it can fall on small tubing or lines and break a line and burn lots of people."

Smoking is forbidden in almost all areas of oil refineries because even the tiniest leak can release highly explosive hydrocarbon vapors. It just does not make sense to smoke where this possibility exists. Yet welding is done in the same areas. Newby says, "There are very few places in our refinery that you can smoke. You can weld just about anywhere. We now weld in areas where they wouldn't even let a man walk through when I hired out there in 1952. Up until the first of this year, I would say our preventive maintenance was gone. We just didn't have any. I can show you stanchions that are rusted off even with the ground that are carrying live 12-inch steam lines. It's been turned in numerous times, but never repaired."

Jack Stagner of the same refinery tells a story that would be amusing if not so frightening. A labor group in an area of the refinery with which it was not familiar looked for compressed air to operate a jackhammer. They opened a likely looking pipe, judged the odorless gas coming out to be air, hooked up their jackhammers and went to work. By a miracle, no sparks were caused by the jackhammer operation. Instead of air, they were using natural gas. Good quality natural gas is odorless in its original form; the distinctive odor the householder smells when there is a leak in his home comes from a chemical deliberately injected into public gas lines as a safety precaution so that leaks will be noticed quickly. The gas in the refinery was kept pure, not odorized, for reasons having to do with the processes in which it was used.

Some plants avoid errors such as this by color-coding all pipe lines. That is, a different color of paint is applied to lines carrying each different thing. Motorists driving along the public highway past this Atlantic Richfield refinery may notice that the distillation towers and other facilities extending two hundred feet or more into the air are painted in varied attractive colors. This is for esthetic reasons; down below fence level, where the men work, paint is not even applied for simple safety purposes.

Attempts to make repairs on units in operation sometimes go to extremes. John Hocking of the American Oil refinery in Texas City provides this example: "On No. 3 pipe still we have a new furnace. It's about two years old and the tube brackets and roof tubes have all either melted or broken or stretched and the tubes are sagging anywhere from six inches to two feet. They have people on top of this furnace at this time cutting holes in there and this is where hydrogen sulfide gas comes from. Anytime you burn a fuel it comes out. They are up there wearing Scott Air Paks trying to reach down with hooks and stop those tubes from sagging, right while we're operating." (Scott Air Paks are air-fed masks which might be compared to those worn by divers.)

Men working in chemical and oil installations are all but unanimous in their assertions that inadequate maintenance of equipment poses constant hazards. Here are a few more examples: Jim Dioneff, Olin Corporation's Ashtabula, Ohio, plant: "Now, we have a caustic scrubber that is in very bad shape. We pound plugs into this poor thing." The scrubber is a device to clean or neutralize toxic or obnoxious gases before they are exhausted up stacks. If 8,000 gallons of phosgene gas stored in this plant should have to be "dumped" in emergency, this scrubber would be depended on to try to neutralize it.

E. W. Van Gunten, Glidden plant in Cleveland: "There is no preventive maintenance performed at all. Everything is emergency repair. If it breaks down, then you rush over and fix it, just temporarily until they get it back into production. It's never fixed right."

Royce Shelton, Velsicol Company, Memphis: "Some of it (the equipment) leaks about all the time—steam leaks, caustic leaks and from time to time various acids."

Ron Loupe, Vulcan Materials, Baton Rouge: "We have acid lines that have been patched a dozen or more times. Fiberglass lines bust and they come back and put a light patch on.

We've had acid lines that just bust wide open. If somebody should happen to be right under, they would just get drenched with acid." This plant was only 16 months old when this statement was made.

A. J. M. Shelton, Humko Products, Chemical Division, Memphis: "Well, patching practices will run the range—tape, matches, screws, so-called Arkansas patches, just about anything you can think of." What is an Arkansas patch? Shelton: "You sharpen a stick and drive it into a leaking line . . . . they just hate to shut anything down. They're production crazy like most companies are."

Peter McIntyre, National Lead, Sayreville, New Jersey: "Now, if that line is running and producing pigment, they will make every effort to patch it up with putty, with tape, with pieces of rubber, a piece of wire, anything short of shutting that line down."

Ray Lovelady, Phillips Petroleum, Kansas City: "There's no such thing as preventive maintenance anymore."

J. E. Powers, Neches Butane Co., Port Neches, Texas: "They're scheduling their turnarounds (shutdowns for overhaul) farther and farther apart." Also: "Recently we had a hydrocarbon line leak and they sent pipefitters over there to put a clamp on it with a piece of rubber over the hole. They tested to measure the thickness of the pipe and their own inspection department admitted it was too thin to be safe, yet they operated it for almost a month."

Oscar Wilson, Union Oil Company, Port Neches: "When they have a turnaround, a big one, the only thing that you can get done is emergency work . . . if you don't have something that is an emergency that will fit into their unit shutdown, they don't touch it."

Such complaints go on and on. Sometimes the maintenance budget is blamed. More often management simply does not want to lose production by taking equipment out of operation. And sometimes lack of manpower is blamed; managers say they cannot obtain the necessary skilled craftsmen—machinists, welders, pipefiteers, electricians, *et al.*—to do the work. Probably it is true that in some situations such skilled workmen are in short supply. In many other localities, they are readily available but management dislikes enlarging the payroll. The matter of immediate availability of craftsmen is somewhat beside the point in industry, for industry creates its own supply of such craftsmen. The procedure generally is quite different from that prevailing in the construction trades.

Construction craftsmen are more or less transient; they work for a while for one contractor, then for another, as old construction projects are completed and new ones begin. These craftsmen learn their trades through apprenticeships lasting three to six years. They are highly skilled and quite flexible. A construction pipefitter, for example, reads blueprints handily and is competent to fit pipe in most any building situation. Construction craftsmen usually are referred to jobs by their unions. The union card is the ticket to employment, since it reflects competence in the craft as well as good standing in the union.

Industrial craftsmen mostly are long-term employees of a single factory and in the majority of cases have learned their skills in that plant. They are not selected by or referred to the employer by the union. Rather, they are hired by company personnel offices while still untrained. The companies try to select young men of good health, reasonable intelligence and high school education who have the potential of becoming skilled and responsible workmen but who at the time of hiring have no specialized training. These untrained young men are at first assigned to unskilled work. As openings occur, they "bid up"—ask for promotion—to positions on the lower rungs of promotional ladders. One such ladder leads to skilled jobs in operating equipment. The other ladder leads to skilled jobs in maintenance, in one of more than a dozen specialized crafts.

The young industrial worker who chooses the maintenance ladder steps into a job as helper to a craftsman and learns his trade at the side of the old-timer, advancing in due course to the top-skill classification. Thus each plant builds up its own work force of craftsmen and steps out into the open market to hire already-skilled craftsmen only in case of rapid expansion of work force or other sudden need.

The failure of management to provide for itself a reservoir of maintenance craftsmen is reflected in a study made by Albert Raymond and Associates, a Chicago consulting firm, as reported in *Chemical Week* magazine of May 13, 1970. E. Truett Newbrough, president of the firm, was quoted as saying, "The maintenance department in the average company is characterized by a serious lack of staff personnel, lack of apprenticeship programs, lack of specialized maintenance technicians and a general lack of measuring and controlling maintenance work." The survey covered 502 companies with 750,000 workers and included 73 firms making chemicals and allied products. It found that 45 percent of the chemical companies responding to the survey had no maintenance training plans.

Starting in the mid-fifties, many plants reduced their maintenance crews and in the process sharply curtailed the training of young craftsmen. Some of the reductions were made without regard to other factors in a simple effort to reduce payrolls. More of them were based on new technology in industry. Automation—quite far advanced in oil operations and in many chemical processes—coupled with the use of larger and more productive facilities gave management a greater financial incentive to keep plants running for long periods of time before shutting down for massive overhauls.

The trend toward widely spaced major "turnarounds" instead of a relatively steady flow of smaller overhaul projects has exaggerated the peaks and valleys of demand for maintenance work. Relatively few mechanics are needed from day to day, relatively many are needed when there is a shutdown of massive, interlocking equipment for overhaul. Cutting their regular maintenance forces to the bone, companies have adopted the practice of calling in outside contractors for the big "turnarounds." Besides depleting the in-plant maintenance crews, this procedure arouses resentment among the craftsmen who are regular company employees. They believe the somewhat transient contractor crewmen are not qualified to work in the plants.

The typical refinery pipefitter says, "Hell, I don't say I could fit the pipe in that skyscraper, but that construction guy who works all the time with clean materials on new buildings is lost when he comes in here and starts fooling around with some of our high-pressure lines and vessels designed to handle just one product. There's nothing else like the things we work with in this plant."

Some of these charges by industrial craftsmen no doubt reflect simple resentment of the competition for jobs posed by outside contractors' crews. Yet credence must be given to the industrial men's arguments that familiarity with the specific plant, its processes, dangers and exotic metals and non-metallic components is an asset. Some recognition of the merits of this view has come from management in very recent years. There has been a slight trend away from contracting-out of repair work back toward usage of more regular company employees.

Haste, as well as use of outside contract employees unfamiliar with a particular plant, is blamed for inadequacy of some turnaround overhauls. Under a schedule perhaps drawn up in a far-away office, a plant will be shut down for a specified number of days for test, inspection and overhaul. Whether or not the repairs can be done thoroughly in that length of time, management tends to start yelling "bolt it up" as the end of the scheduled period approaches.

The Mobil refinery in Augusta, Kansas, was shut down early in April, 1970 for its turnaround. Two weeks time was allowed. R. O. Huddleston, local union secretary, suggests that five weeks would have been more appropriate and notes that a nearby refinery of similar size operated by Skelly consumes five weeks in turnaround.

On April 30, 1970, the Mobil refinery newly returned to

operation was found to have leaks around the head of an iso-butane exchanger inside a cooling tower. Iso-butane is highly explosive. Bob E. Sammons, 41, and Carl Ponder, 55, were sent into the cooling tower to tighten the head. Something caused a spark; explosion and fire followed. Ponder made his way out of the cooling tower, crawling over and around pipes and through water, although he had second degree burns on 25 percent of his body. After the fire was extinguished, Sammons' body was found floating in water in the tower. He may have died instantly in the explosion or he may have been so seriously injured he was relatively helpless, fell into the water, and drowned.

It appears that someone goofed during the two-week shut-down by failing to properly tighten the head of the exchanger. Pointing the finger of blame to any person or persons is not justified, but it must be noted that a mixed crew of outside contractor employees and regular plant employees worked on the task. The mixing of the forces, misunderstandings between the two groups and undeveloped "feel" for the refinery equip-ment by outsiders, as well as the hasty two-week schedule, may have contributed to confusion and the resultant fatal error.

Management must be granted some concessions regarding the financial problems posed by peak-and-valley demand for mechanics for the major overhauls. This scarcely justifies, how-ever, management's frequent slowness to make even routine running repairs with the excuse "we can't find the men." In many localities, skilled men can be hired off the street and in all situations crews could have been kept up to adequate size by the training of new men.

There is not much excuse, for example, for failure of many companies to keep such equipment as motor vehicles in safe condition. In large plants, there are trucks and pickups which never leave the premises, and in many cases these would not pass the safety inspections required by most states for vehicles using public roads.

John Mannino of the Port Arthur Texaco refinery tells of

"this storehouse truck that was braced with a two by four to hold the cab up. The fenders were falling off, no glass in it, the doors were all jagged edged, the brakes were bad." After considerable fussing by the men, the company took it out of operation. Employees of Ashland Oil refinery in Canton, Ohio, say they have vehicles in the plant that would not pass the highway safety check if they were taken onto public roads.

Whether the equipment is large or small, simple or complex, good design and meticulous maintenance are basic necessities if safe and healthy conditions are to be maintained for the workmen. A brakeless truck can kill a man. So can a bursting pipe. Little oozing leaks of toxic fluids or gases can bring illness. Dust or fumes that are not drawn away by exhaust systems can do the same.

Cautious work practices on the part of the men and the women in industry cannot offset all these hazards—hazards created by management's reluctance to spend money.

8

Fewer Men, Running Faster

Productivity of oil refinery workers has doubled since 1958. About twice as much product is pushed through the refineries per man-hour of labor employed because the companies have reduced their work forces while installing larger, more complex process units and adding a considerable measure of automation.

Underground pipelines which transport gasoline and other petroleum products from refineries to market terminals are extensively automated. From these terminals, gasoline is delivered to service stations by larger trucks which rush faster. The pumping of gasoline and other products into trucks at the terminals has been speeded up, in many cases, to a dangerous degree. In the chemical industry, too, there has been a rapid increase in productivity—volume of work performed per man employed.

In nearly all plants of the oil and chemical industries, fewer men are responsible for broader scope operations—and they are none too happy about this. When highly mechanized or automated equipment is working perfectly, life is admittedly easier for all concerned. But when malfunction occurs, men have to use considerable old-fashioned muscle power, and use it hurriedly, to avert explosions or other catastrophes—or to assure the continuance of money-making production. In situation after situation, workmen insist that their crews are too small for emergency situations.

Many oil companies have dispensed with loading rack attendants at terminals where tanker truck drivers pick up loads of gasoline, jet fuel, heating oil and other petroleum products for delivery to ultimate consumers or service stations. Where loaders are on duty, the truck driver approaches the rack, stops, then waits until the loader signals to him before he pulls his truck into position to take on his cargo. Where there are no loaders, the driver simply pulls into position, climbs up on his truck, opens the dome hatches, climbs across to the rack (or platform), swings the pipe (known as a "riser") which carries the product into position over his tank, goes back to the platform and throws a switch to start the flow of product. (Usually he inserts a key to start the flow, which is automatically metered.) As each compartment in his truck is filled, he switches off the pump and moves the riser to another compartment.

The entire process is fraught with danger. The driver may not be overly familiar with a particular loading rack. This may cause him to be slow in reaching a cut-off switch if there is an overflow of highly flammable liquid. He likely doesn't have a "feel" for the rate of flow through the riser—a rate that is supposed to be controlled, but is subject to variance because pumps and other equipment can be temperamental.

A driver under pressure from his employer to make a maximum number of runs may pull his truck hastily into a loading rack position, hit the brakes and cause a spark. This spark can ignite vapors from another truck already being filled, or from spilled products from a previously serviced truck. When a loader is on duty, he ascertains that no spillage or fumes are present before permitting a truck to pull into position. A loader is pretty cautious because he is up on the rack in the danger area and has no desire to get burned.

One or more of the hazards that take place if no loader is on duty prevailed in late 1969 when Thaddeus Kowalski was seriously injured at a Mobil Oil refinery loading rack near Detroit. His truck and another were being filled simultaneously with petroleum products. Kowalski was on top of his truck when a spark ignited spilled fuel or vapors. He was blown 40 feet by the blast. Kowalski was off work several months as a result of his injuries.

J. Roy Johnston, secretary of a Detroit truck drivers' local, contrasts this sort of situation with the more safe procedures followed at a Texaco terminal in Detroit. "At Texaco," says Johnston, "when a second truck pulls up, he can't just fly up underneath this rack until the other truck pulls out and the loader waves the second truck in. The loader will see that there's no spillage on the ground before he waves him in, because a spark can ignite that."

In objecting to the absence of loaders, Johnston points out, "A driver can come in there from out of town and, hell, anything can happen. He doesn't know where the safety shutoff is. Some of the installations want to fill two different units of a truck at the same time by tying the handles down. In fact, Texaco is allowing this."

The risers which discharge products into the tanker trucks are large versions of the nozzles used in service stations to put gasoline into cars, but they don't automatically shut off and they pump at frightfully high speeds. Johnston says, "You're supposed to set the meter to provide the amount you need for your compartment. Let's say you set it for 2,000 gallons. As you come to the last few gallons, it's supposed to slow down. But many times the meter goes over and you've got a spill, you've got a fire hazard. Actually, you're supposed to manually load. You're supposed to have your hand on the shutoff."

In their zeal for faster movement of products, the oil companies have established what they call "speed racks," which pump 600 to 1,000 gallons of product per minute. "If you lift your hand off the control real quickly on these high speed risers," says Johnston, "the pressure can shift to another riser on the rack and this can just knock the guy handling that riser right up into the air."

When drivers, instead of terminal employees more familiar with the equipment, load trucks, they get spills of gasoline and other products on themselves. Severe skin irritations and rashes often result. Gasoline is not a terribly irritating fluid; if a person spills it on his skin, all he needs to do is wash it off within a few minutes. But if his clothing becomes soaked and he must continue to wear the clothing, inflammation of the skin results. In those rare cases where an experienced loader gets his clothing soaked, he ordinarily can take a shower and put on fresh clothing. But the driver subjected to the same sort of spill usually does not have a change of clothing available.

The financial incentive to keep the trucks moving is obvious. A large tanker rig or tractor and tank trailer may cost up to $50,000. License fees are costly. The companies have good reason not to want these trucks delayed for any reason and they face strong temptations not to put a unit into a shop for overhaul.

The short-cuts and speed-ups in trucking are accomplished merely by use of relatively simple mechanical devices and hurry-up attitudes. In large industrial plants, sophisticated automation compounds the problem manyfold. In the entire Ashland Oil refinery in Canton, Ohio, there are only 22 men on duty on the midnight shift, of a total non-supervisory work force of 180. Employees of the plant firmly believe this is not enough manpower, scattered over a 40- or 50-acre plant, to contend with emergencies.

In the Phillips refinery at Kansas City, hard by the city's airport, where approximately 90,000 barrels per day of petroleum is refined into various products, there is a big crude oil distillation unit manned by two men. When it first was put into operation, there were three men. Since then, it not only has been enlarged twice, but the work force is cut by a third. This unit stretches out the length of three city blocks and its towers are menacingly close to landing planes.

Modern mechanization and automation make this possible, if not wise. For maximum efficiency, this unit is designed with a very narrow range of tolerances on operational conditions—temperatures and pressures. Because variance from this range can be dangerous, the engineers designed into it interlock devices to bring about automatic shutdowns if performance strays from the tolerable ranges. But the company apparently is not able to make the big beast operate as the design engineers intended. "So," says Ray Lovelady, local union president, "the interlock systems have all been bypassed or gagged. They stuff rags in the valves—this is what we call 'gagging'—to keep it from shutting down if it goes beyond the tolerances designed for."

The Atlantic Richfield refinery in Houston has a butane recovery unit that once was manned by six men. During a slack period, part of the unit was shut down and the work force was cut from six down to two. When business recovered, the company not only reopened the entire unit but also added another section to it—and kept the work force at two men. Then an entire new unit, which strips a number of products out of crude petroleum, was built adjacent to the butane recovery unit. This new equipment with a separate function was tied in with the butane recovery unit for operational purposes— and one man was added to the work force. Now three men operate facilities at least twice as large and complex as those formerly operated by six men.

Jack Stagner, union safety chairman, says, "I have told the company any number of times that the units are so severely under-staffed that in the event of any serious mishap the operators would have only one course to choose—and that would be the line of least resistance."

You mean right out and over the nearest fence?

Stagner: "Well, figure it out for yourself."

When the company was asked by the union to provide adequate staffing of the unit described, Stagner says management replied, "Well, we do not staff units based on the possibilities of mishaps."

In the American Oil refinery in Texas City, Texas, seven men now operate a distillation unit that replaces three old units manned by approximately 39 men, according to John Hocking, an employee in the plant. The unit covers an area equivalent to about two city blocks. Asked if the operation was not so highly automated that the seven men could just sit in control rooms and watch their instruments, Hocking says, "This is the way they planned it, but it doesn't work out this way. Theory has to give way to reality." Some men still have to inject certain chemicals by hand. One man has about 30 pumps, three compressors and other equipment to constantly inspect. Pumps giving trouble have to be switched off and alternate pumps switched on manually.

Refinery workers concede that when equipment is running smoothly little labor is required. Many operators—paid more for what they know than what they do—go day after day without getting their hands greasy. But they are near unanimous in their assertions that too few men are kept on duty to cope with emergency situations. There are several refinery fires every year in the United States, nearly all of them resulting in some deaths and grave injuries.

In the Vulcan Materials chemical plant at Baton Rouge, a man is alone in a boiler house eight hours each night shift. As long as the boilers are running right and a gauge in a control room shows 250 pounds per square inch pressure on the steam system, no one is concerned about him.

Another man in that plant works alone outside, around carbon tetrachloride, sulfuric acid, caustic, hydrochloric acid and chlorine. Ron Loupe, union negotiations chairman in the plant, says, "If this man was to be overcome by chlorine gas, let's say on the back side of the acid section, it could be an hour or maybe more that he could lay on the ground before somebody would find him."

In the American Cyanamid plant in Kalamazoo, Michigan, there is a lone man who does a job so touchy it is not performed on day shift. Says Lawrence Pease, local union president, "In the alum plant, they have a man who charges the digester with acid at night and puts the steam to it. When he does that, a lot of times the acid comes up and just about out the top of it. He has to stand there and keep adjusting the steam and the air to keep it from coming out. But if it did, there's nobody around there. Nobody checks on him all night. He's completely forgotten. The acid plant operator at least has a check once an hour, but this man on the digester is not checked at all."

Chief Steward Harry Miller adds, "And he can't start putting this acid and alum into the digester—he can't start running it—until after 4:30 when everybody goes home because the acid comes out of the stack up on top when he's heating this stuff up. This stuff is going into the air and it eats the paint off the cars." The reference is to sulfuric acid. As the departing day shift employees move their cars from the parking lot, a small crew of night shift men coming on duty carefully park upwind in preparation for the evening burp of sulfuric acid from the stack.

In small ways, company managers can cut the corners on payrolls to make the balance sheets look better. In the laboratory of National Lead Co. at Sayreville, New Jersey, technicians have to keep several sample checks going at one time. "We have fellows leaving these samples unattended while they're running other samples and these are boiling. Could be a safety hazard if one of them blew when somebody was walking by," says local President John Carney. "They have to run too many samples at one time. A man should stand and watch these things until they have boiled and turn them off before going about other samples."

In 1969, a fire broke out in the Neches Butane plant at Port Neches, Texas. Men on the scene kept the fire from spreading by cooling adjacent equipment with water, but carbon dioxide rather than water was needed to extinguish this blaze fed by leaking hydrocarbons. A truck equipped with carbon dioxide fire fighting equipment was in the plant, but the man assigned to drive it had been sent into town on an errand. The limited crew of regular operators was tied up containing the fire with their water hoses. After a bit of confusion, an electrician who happened to be working overtime and who was not particularly qualified to help the operators control the fire found the CO_2 truck and brought it to the scene. Forty minutes passed before the truck arrived; only five minutes were then required to put the fire out, according to J. E. Powers, who works there.

How much safer it would have been if the company had stood the cost of one man's wages so that quick movement of the truck would have been possible!

About 1,000 people work in the Edmonton, Alberta, plant of Chemcell, Limited (owned by Celanese Corporation of America). There is a plant ambulance, but it is not supposed to leave the plant. Workers requiring hospitalization must be transferred to an outside ambulance at the gate. The reason for this, according to Louis Yakimishyn, chairman of the local union health and safety committee, is that the company does not employ a qualified driver to take the vehicle onto public roads.

Management long has complained of alleged "featherbedding" on jobs and many people who have never been inside an industrial plant accept this often repeated charge as fact. It seldom is fact. Of course nearly everybody in any line of employment, white collar or blue collar, has some slack periods, or sometimes does a little simple loafing. But those whose occupations pose no greater physical dangers than tripping on an office rug should bear in mind that just a few idle hands can be very valuable when suddenly put to work in an emergency situation in an industrial plant.

9

Production Over All

Ernest Rousselle thinks that "Safety Comes First" is only half a slogan. The true but unwritten law in most cases, he says, is "Safety Comes First—Right After Production." Rousselle is in a better position than some to make this judgment. He has worked as a company safety man, a local union officer, and as an International Representative for Oil, Chemical and Atomic Workers. In the latter position he has negotiated with many employers on safety questions.

"The supervisor has to make a decision as to whether to halt production when a question is raised on the safety of continued operation," Rousselle points out. "He asks himself if the situation is unsafe. Then he asks himself if it is unsafe to the point that he must slow down or shut down operations. Nine times out of ten the supervisor is incapable of making the judgment. He is trained to keep production going. He usually is not trained on the technical aspects of what is safe and what is unsafe. Always in the back of his mind is the knowledge that he will be held responsible for the loss of production which will occur if he takes the cautious course of slowing or stopping operations.

"He knows if he chooses the safer alternative, he will lose production. If he takes a chance by continuing to operate, he just *may* have an accident. The pressure is heavy on him to take a chance," Rousselle points out.

If the foreman makes a poor production record, he is subject to demotion or discharge. If, by chance, there is an accident, he may be blamed by higher authorities and fired outright.

He has no union representation, no recourse. He serves at the pleasure of higher management. This is not to suggest that line foremen are to be blamed for a large percentage of the cases of unsafe chance taking. In many cases foremen recommend to area supervisors, shift supervisors or even plant superintendents that operations be stopped for repairs or that other precautionary measures be taken. Often they are overruled.

Frederick A. Linde, who spent 30 years in chemical plant management positions, thinks that intermediate level supervisors are more often to blame for chance taking because they are more gung-ho for production than are line foremen. These intermediate supervisors, holding various positions between the line foremen and the plant management, have hopes and expectations of promotions up the company ladder. They have strong incentives to turn in good records. Most line foremen cannot expect much in the way of promotion.

The line foreman is in the most merciless squeeze. He is closest to and most acutely aware of potential dangers. Yet he is most subject to discharge or demotion and he is constantly subject to having his recommendations overruled. Foremen can be hesitant to ask higher supervisors for permission or advice about correcting a safety hazard if loss of production is involved. To do so may reveal uncertainty to the higher ranking manager. The incentives are to take a chance.

Usually the line foreman has little real authority. He can order such small repairs as can be made from materials at hand—tape, epoxy glue, simple clamps. But a larger action, requiring loss of production or use of more expensive materials and more manpower, must be approved at higher levels. The bureaucratic line of authority can be quite involved, and the more grave the situation, the greater the number of people who have to give approval.

When a process unit has reached the ceiling of safe operation, the foreman must ask a higher supervisor what to do. All too often he is told to keep the equipment operating while trying to lower whatever factors—temperatures, pressures, chemical reactions—are critically near the danger point. Jim Breaux of the American Cyanamid plant near New Orleans describes a case of this sort. "They had a hot spot in this tube through which they pass natural gas and heat it up. Now, I'm told the tube was designed to take temperatures up to about 1100 degrees, but they were supposed to shut down at 800 degrees. They had hourly people (non-supervisors) use some type of chalk to check this tube—you place the chalk on the tube and if it melts, you know it is at a certain temperature.

"I was on the midnight shift when I get a call from a fellow who was afraid to go up there with that chalk. They were running and they knew this thing was possibly going to rupture but they were going to try to run as long as they could. I called the foreman and he said it was safe. I called the plant safety director at his home about midnight. After a while the safety director called back and said supervisors had assured him the tube was safe but promised to check it first thing in the morning. Around three o'clock in the morning this hourly-rated man called back and he says, 'Baby, you almost had you a body. We're down. The thing is ruptured.' He said just fortunately they could bring the plant down with no one getting hurt."

Was this an accident based on honest misjudgment? Not exactly. A plant fireman testified that well in advance of the rupture he had been instructed to stand by with his equipment, not just as a routine precaution, but because *supervision had told him they expected the tube to rupture.* Breaux quotes the fireman as saying, "That man (supervisor) told me to stand by and not even to go make a key round in the plant because they were anticipating this thing would burst and blow the canopy off of the building."

The explosion, when it did come, was more serious than had been calculated. Management denied to Breaux that they anticipated a fire.

Line foremen seldom get bonuses or other specific incentives for pushing production. They simply have jobs to hold. Bottom level foremen in most cases earn only a little more money annually than the highest paid among the men they supervise. Why do they endure this pressure for such small rewards? Most non-supervisory men believe the foremen do so for prestige and social status—in the community, not in the plant. The men in the plant know the score, but ladies at the bridge table do not. When the foreman's wife says, "My husband is in charge of operations in the So-and-So division of the company," it sounds impressive to the other women present. Little do they know that actually he may only supervise half a dozen men and that in this role he has very little authority which is not subject to reversal by the next man up the pecking order. In the sardonic humor of the factory, the foreman often is described as having "all the responsibility and none of the authority."

Widespread charges are made by non-supervisory men that a vast majority of foremen are incompetent. Certainly this is an overgeneralization and no doubt the charges sometimes reflect sour-grape attitudes. There is strong evidence, however, of a growing trend toward selection of supervision on the basis of their pro-production *attitudes,* rather than on the basis of *competence.* In some companies there are many cases of foremen supervising crews doing different types of work than those in which the foremen were trained. This gives rise to much cynicism among the workmen as to the abilities of such foremen and the motivations of higher management in selecting them. The foremen most respected by the men usually are those considered highly competent in the particular skills being supervised. A machinist is quite leery of instructions given by a former bricklayer, and vice versa.

Plant superintendents and plant managers are in a somewhat better situation than either level of management below them. They are in position to have a somewhat broader overview. They can tolerate a little loss of production in one area if other sections of the plant are performing efficiently; the total record can balance off fairly well. The most prevalent criticism of plant managers is that they too often fail to keep informed about conditions in the plant. Preoccupied with front office matters, some of them seldom walk through the working facilities to observe conditions.

Bureaucracy and delegation of responsibilities permit slippage in performance. F. Q. Hood, secretary of the local union representing employees of Universal Oil Products in its Shreveport plant, provides an example: "In the part of the plant where our crews drum catalyst, the fumes are extremely bad. We've asked management to do something about this and they say, 'Well, we're going to shut this part of the plant down and repair all those ovens the fumes are coming from.' It's been several years now that they've been promising this. The day before yesterday I went all the way to the plant manager to try to get him out of his office to go with me over into this area. I told him, 'You wouldn't work in an area like this and we don't think we should ask our people to work in it.' The manager said, 'Well, we just found out that this condition existed.' I said, 'No, this is not right, because I talked to the superintendent of the plant just three weeks ago and tried to get him to do something and they haven't done a thing.' "

Obviously, the union complaints made at lower management levels had not been passed on to the plant manager. And the manager hadn't stirred himself out of his office to survey the situation for himself. Hood says a further step, a threat by the men to quit working, finally brought a reaction. "So today they made a little move to start working on some of the equipment, exhaust fans and what have you in this area," Hood concludes.

At every supervisory level, the overwhelming pressure is to maximize production. In order to do this, risks are taken on health and safety precautions whenever there is conflict. Ernest Rousselle poses the rhetorical question, "Did you ever hear of a plant manager getting promoted because of an outstanding safety record?"

There have been cases of discharge of plant managers after major disasters. Probably in some of these cases corporate headquarters have used the plant managers as scapegoats. A manager should not permit a disastrous situation to develop, but corporate management should share the blame if it has kept the pressure on the manager for high production while not also holding up carrots and brandishing sticks to encourage safety.

Sometimes top plant management simply does not appear to be effective in the direction of its supervisors. In the National Lead Company at Sayreville, after at least two deaths and several illnesses from carbon monoxide and after union investigators found that carbon monoxide detection instruments were set at an unsafe high level, the management made an effort to correct the situation. Not only were all detection devices adjusted to the proper setting, but also foremen were instructed on procedures to follow, being told that if an alarm bell rang indicating too much carbon monoxide present, they were to put on gas masks, go into the area, locate the leakage or whatever caused the alarm to sound, make repairs as necessary, then shut off the alarm only after completing the corrective actions. The plant industrial relations manager so instructed foremen in a letter. "Yet we continue to find foremen who shut off the alarm without finding the sources," says local President Peter McIntyre. Each time the union objected to this procedure, top management reiterated the orders.

"I think," says McIntyre, "that the indoctrination of 30 years that production comes first has penetrated the brain of supervision so thoroughly that nothing else can penetrate."

Any company will avow that it has rules against unsafe procedures, rules that are supposed to be followed strictly by everyone from the newest unskilled workman to the highest management authorities. But rules, in all human affairs, are subject to being bent. A rather remarkable case came when Hurricane Betsy threatened Louisiana as far inland as Baton Rouge four years ago. Andy Wise of the Wyandotte Chemical Company plant at Baton Rouge says, "In our disaster plan we have written out for us step-by-step what we should do in case of hurricane warning. When Betsy hit we followed the plan fairly closely until the point at which plant shutdown was called for—I believe that was when the wind hits 75 miles an hour.

"The glycol department did shut down at that point; the boiler house stayed on the line and the chlorine section stayed on the line until the electric power went off. In the boiler house, we had a wind velocity chart that only records up to 105 miles an hour and the recorder went plumb off the chart, and still they didn't shut down. When the power failed, they then closed the chlorine plant down with flashlights. They disregarded the disaster plan. They tried to keep it on the line."

Few chemical operations are more dependent on an uninterrupted electrical supply than chlorine manufacture. The production units, known as cells, must be kept under a negative pressure; this is done by sweeping the gas from the cells into the header with pumps or "blowers." Even after the power goes off in a cell, chlorine continues to evolve and without the blowers pulling the chlorine away, the gas seeps out of the cells and from pipe leaks. Within 15 seconds of a power failure, the air may be green with chlorine and the shutdown must be performed in masks. There is a serious explosive hazard, too, because of a mixing of hydrogen and chlorine.

The money incentive tempts managers to operate equipment in excess of design capacity. This sometimes brings them into conflict with the technicians who design equipment and the maintenance men who keep it in operating condition. Certainly it keeps pressure on these designers and mechanics. The operations managers press constantly for higher temperatures, pressures, speeds and sizes for the processing of raw materials toward the marketable end product. Technology is challenged to design ever stronger and more dependable equipment to meet these demands.

Almost any new piece of equipment has a rated capacity assigned by the engineers who designed it. After the equipment has operated smoothly at that capacity for a while, operations managers are tempted to increase its load one tentative step after another.

Regarding the DuPont plant at Watson, Alabama, local union President Johnny Cicero says, "In the acid area, the nitric acid plant puts out a lot of fumes that aren't necessary." He does not blame this on leaks resulting from poor maintenance. "I think in one case it is caused by running the machine at an excess of speed," he comments. "I think the equipment is overloaded and therefore it produces excess fumes."

Nick Kostandaras, local union president, says of the Glidden factory in Cleveland: "I think the company pushes some of the equipment to the fullest extent, overworking it. At times equipment will break down and someone is hurt."

In the Muskegon, Michigan, plant of Ott Chemical Company, where phosgene gas has been a persistent problem, union committeeman Roger Lohman says, "A lot of the problem with the phosgene is due to overloading of the scrubbers, trying to run the process too fast." He says the scrubbers (devices in which water and caustic solutions neutralize exhaust gas) are in good operating order, but overloaded. "In the department I'm working in now they just put in two brand new scrubbers. But, still, they put in a bigger scrubber and they try to run the process faster because they have these big scrubbers and they still overload."

Excessive haste is blamed by Bill Parmelee, local president, for another area of trouble which endangers employees at Ott. Small chemical reaction processes are carried out in what is known as the pilot plant area to perfect methods for subsequent use in commercial scale operations. "The pace seems to be 'quick push' in that pilot plant," Parmelee notes. "Those operators out there are operating reactors that people in the main plant wouldn't dream of running. Their setups are shabby. We had a terrific explosion there two months ago. It blew the whole wall out, although it was only a 30-gallon reactor. It blew up because they didn't have adequate metering devices to meter in the material that was causing the reaction. The

consequence was that 90 percent of the material that was supposed to go in over a period of an hour or two was injected in
about two minutes."

The First Commandment spoken to Moses says, "Thou
shalt have no other gods before me." In modern American
industry the name of the Number One god is Production and
management is faithful in following him. In many, many cases
production is increased without corresponding expansion of
auxiliary equipment. Charles Valerio, union safety committeeman in the titanium sponge manufacturing plant of Reactive
Metals, Incorporated, Ashtabula, Ohio, says, "The dust condition is now worse because the tonnage is greater. Prior to
1966, we ran about 300,000 pounds per month. Now it's about
a million and a half pounds per month. I would say they are
overloading their conveyor belts."

Management in this titanium plant intermittently faces
the problem of balancing safety against $20,000. A device
called a reducer, in which the titanium ore is ground up prior
to further processing, sometimes jams up because a chunk of
ore gets caught between the stationary and the moving parts
of the grinding equipment. Management then may dump the
load of material out, at a cost the workmen believe to be $20,000
in time and materials, in order to free the jammed machinery.
Or, management may elect to try to apply brute force to the
machine's drive shaft in order to break the jam.

Usually, management takes the less expensive course. Men
are assigned to twist the drive shaft with pipe wrenches. To
increase leverage, "cheaters" are applied to the pipe wrenches.
A cheater is simply a piece of pipe stuck over the wrench handle
to make the handle longer and the leverage therefore greater.
As the men heave, torque builds up in the shaft to the point that
it is likely to spring back, spinning the cheater-extended pipe
wrenches violently back toward the men. At the insistence of
the union, the company did build a platform on which the
men could stand while performing this job, thus giving them

more maneuvering room to dodge the reverse kick of the wrenches.

"Since then," recalls Lawrence Scafuro, "Jim Gregg has had a lacerated chin, Brother Gluvna has had his chin ripped open, the general foreman has hurt his arm, and our production foreman had a broken arm."

There is a third alternative the company probably could take to eliminate this bone-breaking procedure. A mechanical means could be devised to force the drive shaft free. "I suggested this," says Scafuro. "When I worked on board ship as an engineer, we had turning jacks to turn our engine over. There was a gear on the shaft and you could disengage it, as well. I suggested something like this in our plant, but they have never come up with a solution."

Workmen in many plants report cases of stepped-up production without corresponding increases in capacity of health-protecting devices such as exhaust fans to carry away dust and fumes. Of the Goodyear Tire & Rubber Company chemical division plant in Niagara Falls, union safety chairman Richard Credicott says, "When this plant first started out, I understand it was a small operation, but it's getting bigger as it goes. While they're expanding the capacity, they're not getting dust collectors to take care of it."

Of the Olin Company chemical plant in Niagara Falls, local union President Francis Strong says, "The men want to get this gas and dust out so they don't have to breathe it. In some cases we have openings in the roof, but that doesn't take care of it. They don't have facilities such as suction fans. It's just not adequate for the amount of product (a chlorination material for swimming pools) they are making. It was adequate years ago."

Asked if capacity of the equipment was being overloaded, Strong says, "They claim they are running normally. But at times they have to get this stuff out. Every so often they say we're going to higher tonnage. Such as in our dryers—they're talking about 70 tons and I think it was 35 tons they were supposed to be handling." The company has indicated that it intends to add new machines "in the future" to accommodate the larger load.

The Houston Chemical Company plant at Beaumont, Texas, processes ethylene, ethylene oxide, ethylene glycol, bromine and tetraethyl lead. All are hazardous materials, particularly the tetraethyl lead. "We are continuously exposed to some part of the tetraethyl lead," says Harlin Harrison, union chairman. Even so, there is evidence that management considers uninterrupted production more important than health protection precautions.

"We've had several cases where operators would be running their equipment and have extreme contamination leaks or spillage and they've tried to shut down but management has made them continue to run," reports Harrison. "They make you go ahead and run until the next day. They won't put enough people on night shifts to handle the situation." The union has asked the company to put in better seals around bearings on some old equipment which leaks fumes, but, says Harrison, the company replies that "it costs too much money."

Employees of Allied Chemical Company at Moundsville, West Virginia, were asked in January, 1970, to clean and make repairs on chlorine producing cells while wearing gas masks—masks which originally had been intended for emergency use only. "So you can see these companies are not safety conscious, they are production conscious," comments Sam Lopez, international union representative.

Fred Carraway, local union vice president in the Montrose Chemical Company plant in Newark, says, "Management seems to be interested now solely in top production, pleasing the stockholders."

The management viewpoint is perhaps best summed up by an official of Union Carbide Company. Don Kreuter, a local union leader in Carbide's Tonawanda, New York, plant, says: "I have approached management numerous times on health matters and the answer was, 'Well, we're not in the business of safety, we're in the buiness of making molecular sieves.' This is a quote. It is from Robert Langerhans, one of the division bosses."

10

Hard Hats and Goggles

Most managers assert that they are deeply concerned with the health and safety of their employees. Most of them are undoubtedly sincere. But for a manager to take really effective action to protect his employees puts him squarely into conflict with his basic role in the profit system. Production—and the achievement of more and more and more production—is the duty of operating managers who direct most work forces. At higher company levels, the concern and duty of management broadens to include not only production but also sales, minimization of costs and other elements which maximize profit. Profit—more gently alluded to as "earnings" in corporate reports —is the sole reason for existence of the corporation.

Managers obliged to concentrate on production, cost control, and profit simply cannot be zealous in the pursuit of non-productive, non-profitable goals such as achieving optimum health and safety conditions. To stop a production process in order to repair a line or vessel which is leaking a toxic material can cost much money. To kill a man may well be cheaper. Even an open and shut case of job-caused death likely will cost the company not more than $25,000 in the average state.

Louis Yakimishyn was made ill in the Chemcell, Limited, plant at Edmonton, Alberta, about March 1, 1970, from exposure to acetic acid, methanol, acetone and methyl acetate. Because he was suffering from severe headaches and temperature, his doctor ordered him to bed, where he was immobilized eight days. Yakimishyn blames his exposures and the resulting illness on a leaking pump. He quotes a company supervisor as saying, "We would have fixed that pump before, but we make a hundred thousand dollars a day on that little unit and we couldn't afford to shut it down."

Of course there probably is not a manager in North America who would knowingly cause or permit a death even to save a million dollars. But the financial incentive pressing on managers to take risks leading to possible illness, injury or death are overwhelming. Management spokesmen testifying before legislative bodies assert that they have financial incentives as well as humanitarian reasons for maintaining safe and healthful work places, but this is not quite true. By and large, it pays to operate equipment until it collapses rather than keep it in constantly good repair. To make repairs for health and safety sake is a nonproductive cost item.

True, management has an incentive to avoid fires which destroy extensive sections of a plant and interrupt production, or disasters which kill or maim large numbers of people and thereby soil the company's public image. Fear of fires motivates most companies to pay more attention to fire-fighting drills than to first aid or medical services. Concern with the public image is the reason management safety manuals often have sections devoted to advice on the handling of press relations in case of large-scale accidents.

For management to act sternly in protecting the health and safety of employees would constitute self-policing against management's own basic interests. Self-policing is too much to ask of frail humanity. And managers are human.

Flying in the face of this conflict of interest, American companies generally oppose having the employees' health and safety conditions policed by any other agencies, such as unions or government. Management insists on retaining this responsibility unto itself. This, too, is a human attitude. No one likes to have other people meddling in his affairs, be they traffic patrolmen, income tax auditors, credit investigators or health and safety inspectors.

Having generally succeeded in excluding other forces from

the field of industrial health and safety, management feels some compulsion to carry on its own safety programs. Since true self-policing is unpleasant, somewhat unnatural, and in conflict with the basic objective of maximizing profit, such management safety programs tend to take the form of "making the other fellow do right." Company programs usually concentrate on advising the employees to avoid accidents—obvious, visible accidents—more than creeping health injuries. These programs do little to correct management's own shortcomings, despite the evidence that most illnesses and injuries are management-caused rather than the result of human errors by non-supervisory workers.

Typically, management takes a "hard hat and safety goggles" approach. Workmen are harangued to wear their hard hats all the time and their safety glasses or goggles in many situations—even those in which they can do more harm than good.

The only substantial benefit from wearing hard hats is protection from falling objects. This makes such hats valuable for men engaged in multi-story construction work, where tools or pieces of material may be dropped. Hard hats are of little if any value to those industrial workmen who never work where there is a danger of falling objects, but tens of thousands of such workmen are required to wear them eight hours per day.

Goggles or safety glasses are eye-savers for men working with some types of metal working tools, grinding equipment, or other devices which may throw off bits of material and likewise for men who may be exposed to acid spills. But these glasses or goggles may be more dangerous than helpful to a man climbing a ladder through a fog of innocuous steam vapor which condenses on the lenses and blinds him.

Asked if the employees of the American Oil refinery at Sugar Creek, Missouri, got safety training, local union Secretary Robert Sanford says there is little training but, "They tell them what they have to do, like wearing safety glasses and hard hats."

Of the safety efforts of management in the Glascote Products plant in Cleveland, local union Vice President George D. Shiner says, "It seems that as long as you're wearing your safety glasses, that's all that matters. It doesn't matter if an air line is laying across the aisle or a 440-volt electric line is laying across the aisle or what have you. This is all right as long as you're wearing your safety glasses. This is about the extent of their safety program."

Does this company have a safety officer?

Shiner: "They claim they have a safety man."

LeRoy Hale, local union secretary, points out that this official devotes only part time to this effort—he also is plant engineer. Says Hale, "Whenever we'd have our safety committees go around with him monthly, every time we'd have the same list of problems to show him. And he'd say, 'Well, this is being done,' or 'This is being ordered.' And there would be nothing done about it. Safety glasses is about the only thing that they're really hot on."

Ray Henderson, welder in the Tonawanda, New York, plant of Union Carbide, says, "You are required to wear a hard hat and the company feels as if you're safe as long as you have your hard hat and safety glasses on."

What does your safety director concentrate on?

Henderson: "Practically nothing. A couple of years ago we had a man killed. A painter was killed working with a spray gun. Static electricity or something caught the paint on fire and he died later in the hospital. Now, they had me welding near open containers of paint thinner and paint. I objected to welding near these open containers. It was brought to the attention of the company safety man. He did nothing. I finally went to the general foreman and demanded that those open containers be moved and they were moved that day. We already had one man killed and I didn't want to be the second one."

Safety glasses and hard hats are inexpensive but they are tangible. At little cost, a company can present visual evidence of its desire to protect the employees—while more dangerous hazards remain uncorrected. For a few dollars a company can buy a rubber suit, boots, gloves and mask for a man who must periodically expose himself to leaking acids. It would cost more to re-design or repair the equipment so that it would not leak. Little paper or felt masks costing a few pennies keep some dust out of a man's respiratory system; exhaust systems to pull the dust away from the man can cost thousands of dollars.

And, costs aside, the commands to wear hard hats, goggles, rubber suits and masks shift the burden from management to the employees. Discipline of other people comes easier than discipline of oneself. Painting over and making pretensions come easier than remedying basic problems.

Good "public relations" may be the root cause for most companies concentrating on visible, simple safety. Like all professions and all trades, all industry structures itself and develops its own mores. It has its own code and its own system of acclaim. The National Safety Council, and various industrial groups, are prolific givers of awards. A plant manager can get an impressive-looking plaque or a banner for the plant flag pole, and maybe his picture in some trade journal for "an outstanding safety record." It is not too hard, for the rules are simple and there is little real scrutiny of the records.

On the other hand, why should the plant manager concern himself with long range health? He really does not understand it. There are no immediate payoffs and no flattering articles in trade journals for developing a *health* program.

Plant managers are mobile creatures. Most are transferred frequently and many are fired in the hard competition of the industrial world. The Olin Corporation plant in Ashtabula, Ohio, has had six managers in six years. These transient managers need something to establish their bonafides at their next assignment, and a health program will not do it. Being mobile, these managers sense that they will not have to live with the poor health of their employees and former employees; they can "sleep at night" without knowing long range health problems. Falls, fires and massive chemical spills are something else. They produce immediate, visible and disagreeable injuries and deaths.

It is part of the plant manager lore that he must charge out to the scene of an accident and visibly assume charge, whether he really can contribute anything or not. No one likes carnage and it is a rare manager, indeed, who is able to keep his cool in sight and smell of burnt flesh or torn limbs. And so, no doubt buried deep in the subconscious, is the desire to minimize such unsightly things as violent injury or death. Therefore, emphasis is placed on routine, visible safety.

Beneath the plant managers who hold really decisive authority, there are in many larger plants safety directors who are supposed to keep conditions safe and healthful. Many of them know that the "hard hat and goggles" approach is superficial and there are indications that some of them are very frustrated men.

For once, let us quote a statement anonymously, as a matter of common kindness toward the man involved. A workman in a large plant, when asked what the company safety man does, replies, "That's a good question. Everybody in the plant would like to know what he does." And from across the room comes another voice: "He drinks." Perhaps the man drinks because of a guilty conscience. Says the local union secretary, "This safety man hasn't got the power that he should have. You bring a safety condition to his attention and he may agree with you on the spot. But the plant manager or the personnel director will always override him. He hasn't got the power to make a decision."

In the Universal Oil Products Company plant in Shreveport, where 300 men handle deadly chemicals, the personnel director was doubling in brass as a safety director as of January, 1970. Previously, the plant had a full-time safety manager.

The author asks, "When you did have a safety manager, did he make an effort on the fumes and dust problem, or was he more of a hard hat and goggles guy?"

Says F. Q. Hood, local union secretary: "When he first

came into the plant, he gave us the indication that he was really interested and was really going to do big things. I think the top people told him he was just going to do what they told him to, just as little as possible, and as far as I know he was not very successful in getting any real changes made." This apparently sincere safety man does not work there anymore.

The Jefferson Lake Petrochemical Company plant near Calgary, Alberta, is an extraordinarily dangerous installation because of constant presence of hydrogen sulfide gas and other forms and derivatives of sulfur. Natural gas from wells in that vicinity contains about 30 percent H_2S—very poisonous. The Jefferson Lake plant takes the hydrogen sulfide out so that the remaining clean "sweet" gas can be piped eastward across Canada for domestic and commercial use. Commercially marketable sulfur is extracted from the hydrogen sulfide.

There are leaks and other problems with the H_2S. Workers in the plant recall six or seven men out of the work force of about 70 who were overcome by the gas during 1969. Naturally, they are concerned with taking every possible precaution against exposure to it. They believe that currently they have a good man as company safety director. "But," says an employee, "I've been told he has only so much money to work with and he can't overdo his money. He has a budget to run by and they won't allow him to go over his budget."

Asked if he thinks the safety director in the Reactive Metals Incorporated metals reduction plant in Ashtabula, Ohio, really tries to do a job, Charles Valerio, union safety committeeman, says, "I can't say if he really tries or not. I know that if he would try, he would get his ears pinned back. So, he just forgets about it."

Of the Port Arthur, Texas, refinery of Texaco, John Mannino, union committeeman, says: "The company safety department has four men and a clerk. They haven't got any teeth to bite. What I mean is that they couldn't walk up and stop a job if it was unsafe, because I think management has pretty well trained them."

Jack Stagner, union safety chairman in the Houston refinery of Atlantic Richfield, says the company safety director is an astute person, active and ambitious, "But the thing of it is that the safety department director has no power. He cannot do anything."

Do you suppose he's under pressure from the plant manager to not do things that would slow down production?

Stagner: "That sums it up real good."

It is perhaps because of frustration that some safety directors become preoccupied with hard hats and goggles. Vetoed by plant managers when they recommend costly correction of hazardous conditions, they turn to the easier approaches where they can do a little good and make some sort of showing in return for their monthly salaries.

Winfred Lawery, union grievance committeeman in the Monsanto plant at Trenton, Michigan, says, "That company safety man doesn't have any more to say around there than I do. He runs around there and he says he's going to take care of this and take care of that. When he can get the maintenance department to move, well, he can get a few things done. I believe that we as a union committee sometimes have more leverage than he does."

Frustration, certainly on the union side and apparently on the company safety man's side, has crippled efforts to clean up this Monsanto plant. Adam Caban, local union vice president, tells of union members who have quit the joint union-management safety committee because of a feeling of futility. "They just couldn't get anything done," says Caban. The principal complaint at Monsanto is inadequate maintenance, particularly of exhaust systems which are supposed to draw rash-causing dusts out of the factory. Caban describes one particular place in the plant where the exhaust system once was so strong it would suck a pack of cigarets out of a man's pocket, but now is so weak it barely will draw away the smoke from a cigaret. Apparently either the exhaust ducts are clogged or there is an opening somewhere which destroys the air flow.

Monsanto employees report frequent leaks of ammonia, phosphoric acid, nitric acid, ethylene oxide and caustic, all of which are harmful to health. Winfred Lawery says plant sewers plug up, causing the various acids and chemicals mixed with water to flood out on the floors. "When it builds up enough it's like a geyser," says Lawery. "It'll just come over and spill all over the shipping department floor." (The sewer system to which he refers is separate from the sanitary sewer which serves toilets).

These conditions are examples of what company safety men in most cases cannot correct. The typical safety director can order the workmen to wear boots, goggles or hard hats, but he cannot order the manager to spend money on equipment that would make the boots and goggles unnecessary.

Don Courtney of Wyandotte Chemical Company, Baton Rouge, presents this same picture in another way. "If the safety director sees an employee doing something that's not right, he's very quick to bring attention to it," says Courtney. "But when the employee brings to the attention of the safety director the question 'What can you do about the chlorine in there?' the supervisor says, 'Well, we're going to do something,' and that's the end of it. He's gone."

William Bowers, president of the local union representing employees of J. T. Baker Chemical Company at Phillipsburg, New Jersey, says that cost is the eternal bugaboo when safety questions are raised. "From the safety engineer's own standpoint, in his own words, his hands are tied," declares Bowers.

What does this safety engineer do?

Bowers: "Well, mostly he writes articles for safety magazines, such as the one I have here entitled 'Occupational Hazards for 70,000 Plants,' and this had to do with the noise in this plant." Then Bowers goes into a long, detailed enumeration of the noise hazards that remain in the Baker facility.

Ernest Rousselle, the union representative who has had experience on both sides of the union-management fence, explains that the problem is based on the structure of management. The safety engineer may report a hazardous situation, but the plant manager makes the decision as to whether to spend the money taking corrective action. The manager has other preoccupations and incentives. He doesn't have to work in the hazardous place.

In some companies, the safety director theoretically has some authority over lower level supervisors. He may in such cases be authorized to challenge an operation. But Rousselle points out that whenever the safety engineer confronts a supervisor, the supervisor almost inevitably goes on the defensive and offers excuses or explanations. Arguments, rather than remedies, often result. This is another manifestation of human frailty by the human beings in the ranks of management.

The conflict of interest between working conditions and profit maximization takes an even more direct form when, as is the case in many plants, the safety director has other managerial duties. In the Olin Corporation plant at Ashtabula, according to David Baird, union safety committeeman, the company has "a safety director once in a while." Baird explains, "In the summertime, he's a pusher for kids that come in out of college to work, painting the plant. He's the maintenance pusher more than the safety supervisor."

In the General American Transportation Corporation terminal in Carteret, New Jersey, Frank Peter complains, "There hasn't been a safety meeting held in our plant since last June or July, almost six months. When the safety committee went up to management and asked for a meeting, the management would say, 'Well, there's no time.' It seems like production was coming first before the safety of the men in the plant."

What does the company safety director do with his time?

Peter: "Well, he's, I guess, more in production, canning, personnel director. He has more than one function."

Men in the Ashland Oil Company refinery at Canton, Ohio, point to a long list of uncorrected hazards reported to the company. Asked what the company safety man concentrates on, Harold Wilson, union safety chairman, says, "He concentrates mostly on production."

Richard Credicott, union safety chairman in the Goodyear Tire & Rubber Co. chemical plant in Niagara Falls, also finds corporate objectives in conflict with health and safety activities. Queried about the attitude of the management, he says, "Well, they try to preach health and safety to you, but I don't think they are 100 percent sincere. I mean, they go along with a few things, but if it's something that's going to cost them money, they try to get out of it."

Managers often speak of encouraging attitudes of safety among workers, but management actions often cause negative attitudes. Julius N. Jacobsen, a union leader in American Cyanamid's big plant near New Orleans, has devoted many years to safety. He has gone to night classes at Delgado College to study the subject. He attends conventions of the National Safety Council and has been the recipient of awards from that organization.

A gentle, mature man, Jacobsen sometimes gets discouraged, both with management and with his fellow workers. The company has an extensive safety department, but the men become frustrated with delays in correction of hazardous situations. Says Jacobsen, "When an hourly worker reports an unsafe condition to his supervisor, the supervisor may agree, he may not agree. If he does agree, he takes so long before he has the condition corrected that the man develops the attitude, 'Why should I report anything else? I've reported this and the condition still exists.' The attitude of the workers is nil, safetywise."

Worker morale also can be offended by condescending attitudes on the part of managers. Jack Stagner, Atlantic Richfield employee, Houston, describes management attitudes in response to workers' suggestions: "It's just like they were talking to some small child they don't really want to get involved with, or they really don't know the answer. You just pat a child on the head and tell him, 'Okay, we'll take care of it.'"

Regarding hydrogen sulfide fumes circulated into control rooms of Shell refinery, Pasadena, Texas, through air conditioners, L. E. Sanford says: "It gets quite nauseating at times. Yes, we've mentioned it to management and most every time it is mentioned to them they come back with some sort of sarcastic answer. They seem to me sarcastic, like 'If we don't like the air conditioning, we can get outside where it's hot.' " Of course these men cannot perform their control room duties while outside the room.

Company safety efforts, especially in small companies, sometimes appear rather pathetic. The Montrose Chemical Company plant in Newark, New Jersey, has only 55 non-supervisory workers, but they handle several deadly poisons. On bulletin boards in this plant are posted hand-lettered charts labeled "First Aid Measures—Quick Reference Facts." There are three sheets of these, hand-lettered crossways on 8½ x 11 inch ruled paper. Twenty-four hazardous materials are enumerated.

Column 1 of the charts names the material, column 2 its physical state, column 3 tells what action to take in case of exposure by inhalation, column 4 what action to take after skin contact and column 5 what to do in case of exposure to eyes.

Regarding malanonitrile, the neatly hand-lettered chart advises, "Have cyanide kit available." It notes that the material can be in solid, liquid or vapor form. In case of inhalation, the advice is "If symptoms of cyanide poisoning appear, use amyl nitrile ampules, give emergency oxygen, get immediate medical help." In case of skin contact: "Wash area with large amounts of soap and water, remove contaminated clothing." In case of exposure to eyes: "Flush continuously for a full 15 minutes with water, get medical help."

Get medical help? In case of accident in that plant, the man is put in a car driven by one of his co-workers and taken to a medical center near Newark airport. When a man had his eyes burned by monochloroacetic acid in this plant late in 1969, it took almost an hour to get him to the medical center, according to Fred Graham, local union secretary.

Monochloroacetic acid is identified as a medium range toxic on a short-range basis, long-term effects unknown. When overheated, it emits highly toxic fumes of phosgene and chlorides. Malanonitrile is not listed in standard chemical dictionaries; it is one of those thousands of strange new products.

Give Montrose some credit. At least someone in local management took the pains to hand-letter those safety charts. In most plants, there are no charts whatsoever providing the workmen with quick advice for meeting chemical emergencies. Such safety posters as do appear generally present slogans, nothing more, when the real need is for information.

Montrose management refuses to install monitoring devices to detect the presence of toxic gases. Charles Johnson, union safety chairman, says, "They won't give us any reason why. They say that expense doesn't mean anything but they're too complicated, and they give us the answer that DuPont doesn't use them. But we're thinking about our own safety." Even though the Montrose plant is quite small, Johnson is excused from his regular duties pretty much full time to work on safety in the plant. The company safety man who presumably hand-lettered those charts also is personnel manager. It would appear to be a case in which people are making some efforts to protect working conditions, but are lost in the miasma of ignorance that surrounds modern chemicals.

And it is ignorance, among supervisors at the operating levels as well as among workmen, which perhaps explains why management efforts are directed more to routine safety than to health protection.

Regarding the Farmers Chemical Company plant at Joplin, Missouri, where two men quit work in late 1969 upon advice of physicians because of sulfuric acid fume damage to their internal organs, local union President Leo Simonds says of the management approach, "They have an energetic safety committee, but this safety pertains to accidents. They seem to neglect the angle of inhaling fumes and dust."

Some workmen blame lack of knowledge on the part of the bosses for management avoidance of the health issue. But others believe there is deliberate concealment of the known facts. Foremen have been heard to say—perhaps frivolously or ignorantly rather than as an expression of company policy—that if the men really knew what they were working with they would just walk off the job. Some workmen charge that company officials make light of possible health hazards because the men would demand higher pay if they knew what the dangers were.

Whatever the motivation, managers often are evasive when questioned as to the chemical content and the potential health hazards of various materials. And whatever the motivation, management indicts itself by rather consistently refusing to take protective steps based on well-known scientific and engineering procedures. A specific example is the failure to use automatic monitoring devices to detect the presence of deadly gases. These instruments are available from equipment supply houses, but very few of them can be found in industrial plants.

Possibly the original industrial monitoring device for toxic gas is the canary bird, a creature apparently more susceptible to some or many of the poison fumes than man. It used to be that canaries were kept around potentially gassy places in mines and in industrial plants—and perhaps they still are in some cases. The men watched the bird, and if the bird died it was a signal to the men to evacuate.

In a more informal way, employees of the U. S. Army's Rocky Mountain Arsenal near Denver keep their eyes on the rabbits. This controversial installation, located just north of Denver's busy airport, is the storage site for the Army's vast supplies of odorless, tasteless and deadly nerve gas. There is considerable open space around, so wild rabbits are present. When too many dead rabbits are found, the workmen redouble their search for possible leaks of nerve gas.

The canary and the rabbit may be suitable early warning agents against the approach of fatal concentrations of poisonous or asphyxiating fumes. They are hardly precise enough to measure concentrations which, while tolerable for short periods, wreak slow but persistent damage on the human body.

Chlorine, the most commonly used industrial gas, is considered damaging to health in concentrations of more than one part per million in air over an eight-hour work day, according to the American Conference of Governmental Industrial Hygienists. It is detectible by odor at 3.5 parts per million. Fifty parts per million is dangerous for brief exposure but something on the order of 1,000 parts per million are required to cause quick death. The time to get away from chlorine is not when the birdies die but much sooner.

There are electronic devices which can monitor the presence of chlorine, as well as hydrogen sulfide, ammonia, carbon monoxide, hydrogen cyanide and many other dangerous gases. These can be calibrated to ring alarm bells at whatever level of concentration is deemed to be above safe limits. This type of monitor can be attached to the wall in any area where gases may be present. It provides automatic, 24-hour-per-day surveillance. Few of these devices are used in American industry, if responses made to this reporter by hundreds of workmen may be taken as a representative sample.

Frederick A. Linde, assistant to President A. F. Grospiron of the Oil, Chemical and Atomic Workers, draws from his 30 years of experience as a chemical engineer and as a manager in the production phase of industry to explain at least one reason why this is so. While the automatic monitors are not particularly expensive, they are delicate instruments which must be checked, adjusted and repaired quite frequently. This maintenance chore is a nuisance. It does nothing to increase production. It also is just possible that some managers object to using the monitors because they do not wish to alarm the workers. When alarm bells ring, workers have a tendency to move toward the exits, a very unproductive procedure.

Considerably more common around industrial plants are simple instruments variously called "sniffers" or "dragger tubes." These are small hand-held devices resembling bicycle pumps. Filter papers sensitive to the particular gas being evaluated are inserted. When the pump plunger is pulled, air and whatever is in the air is drawn through the filter. The resulting discoloration of the filter indicates the degree of concentration of the gas being checked. Mine Safety Appliance Company advertises one of these devices which it says can measure concentrations of more than 130 different toxic gases, vapors and mists.

These sniffer devices are suitable for spot checks of suspected concentrations of hazardous chemicals in the atmosphere. They hardly suffice for day-long monitoring unless a man stands in the spot of exposure all day long and takes samples at frequent intervals.

A still more commonly used device is the explosimeter. Again using the bicycle pump principle, this gadget can draw an air sample and measure the concentration of explosive gases. These are quite regularly used to determine if potentially explosive vapors remain in tanks or vessels men are about to enter to make repairs, especially when those repairs involve welding or other work which could ignite vapors. Explosions, it must be noted, not only kill people but also wreck valuable equipment and halt production. The economic imperative is to avoid explosions. There is little, if any, economic incentive to avoid slow poisoning or tissue damage from lower concentrations of harmful substances.

In the Airco Chemical Corporation plant at Calvert City, Kentucky, men complain of fumes from vinyl acetate and methanol. Vinyl acetate is a skin irritant that under certain conditions also is a narcotic. Methanol is common wood alcohol; it is a strong narcotic and a cumulative poison when it slowly builds up in the body. There is no monitoring for gases in this plant, according to Bob Terry, local union president.

In the ferro-alloys plant of Union Carbide at Alloy, West

Virginia, workmen are exposed to chlorine. J. W. Simmons, a local union leader, says this chlorine smell is present "at all times, 24 hours a day, seven days a week." Men have passed out and have been hospitalized due to chlorine inhalation. There are many cases of emphysema, bronchial trouble and asthma among the employees. "There is no monitoring of gases, fumes or dust on a regular basis," says Simmons.

In Union Carbide's Clarksburg, West Virginia, plant, where local union President Percy Ashcraft says disability retirements and early retirements exceed normal age 65 retirements, the union asked management to permit the union to bring its own monitoring devices into the plant. Management declined, saying that the officials would let the men know if there were any hazards. In the same company's Marietta, Ohio, ferro-alloys plant, management has done some air sampling, and has told union officers that conditions were safe, but would not let the union men see the sampling records, according to Jim Ratcliff of the local union.

J. W. Carpenter, local union president, says that in the Geigy Chemical Company insecticide and herbicide plant at McIntosh, Alabama, there is no monitoring except for hydrogen cyanide. He clarifies this point by saying that even the hydrogen cyanide concentrations are checked only after workmen smell the gas. There is no dust monitoring, even though the dust is sometimes "so thick you can't see 50 feet" in the herbicide formulation department, according to Carpenter.

This plant has an interesting safety device. There are windsocks on tops of buildings. In case of major leaks of dangerous fumes, the men are instructed to glance at the windsocks and run up-wind, or cross-wind. There is no time to hold a wet finger in the air.

A further recitation of examples where monitoring is not done is pointless. In most plants, it is not done. Company safety departments concerned with hard hats and goggles seldom venture into this field of health protection. And some companies do not even pay much attention to elementary safety precautions. Management of the edible oils division of Humko Products in Memphis, Tennessee, declined even to recognize a union safety committee. Union Representative Hugh Owen says, "In negotiations, management said that they hired the men out there to perform the production and not be safety men and that it 'would be too expensive an item.'" Humko's other Memphis plant, the chemical division, does a little better. Says A. J. M. Shelton of the local union, "If a department goes a month without having a lost-time accident, each man in the department is given two cups of coffee."

This is just a particularly absurd example of a petty approach to an overwhelming problem. Beyond cup-of-coffee rewards and hard hat and goggles commands, there is needed more chemical and medical research, more training, extensive—and admittedly expensive—improvements in equipment and operating methods, and the sharing of responsibility for policing of health and safety conditions.

11

The Veterinarians

George Evans, a leader in the Chemical and Crafts Union in Union Carbide's big plant at Bound Brook, New Jersey, says of the company doctor: "We call him the vet."

In clarification, Evans adds: "I think he is well-qualified, but after all he is a company doctor."

Bob Diehl of the same plant comments, "Well, that's George's opinion. My opinion is somewhat lower." Diehl and Evans cite several cases in which the company doctor made wrong diagnoses of workers' illnesses.

The attitudes expressed by Evans and Diehl are harsh. They may be unfair. But they are quite typical of the general lack of respect held for company doctors by working men. Fred Carraway, local union vice president for employees of Montrose Chemical Company in Newark, says, "A horse is given a better examination than we're given by the company doctor."

Most workers are convinced that physicians serving the employers consistently interpret their findings so as to protect the company, rather than in such way as to best serve the patient. Charles Johnson, union safety chairman in the Montrose plant, says: "Two weeks ago we had a brother named Martel Johnson who went to his doctor, complained of chest pains, eyes running, couldn't sleep at night. His doctor told him he shouldn't work in that particular department. The company in turn sent him to a company doctor who says the man is all right. But Johnson says he doesn't want to work in there. They discharged this man; they didn't give Johnson a choice of assignment to a different job."

Company doctors can find all sorts of non-occupational reasons for illnesses. Sometimes their so-called medical diagnoses fly in the face of empirical facts, as in a case in the Shell Chemical plant at Pasadena, Texas. Says Roy Barnes, local union president: "Over in the phenol section they have a lot of fumes. They make ethyl chlorohydrin, which will tear up your skin. We had one fellow over there who went to the company doctor about his skin troubles and was told he was allergic to sunshine. Yet, when he would go out fishing on his long change (in effect, long weekend) and stay out in the sunshine this thing would get well because he'd be away from the plant." L. E. Sanford of the adjoining Shell Oil refinery comments, "It seems like about the only thing that the company doctor knows is a potential hernia or a potential bad back. If you don't have a potential hernia, he'll give you one when he examines you."

Poison ivy is blamed many times by the company doctor for rashes frequently occurring among employees in the Geigy Chemical Company plant at McIntosh, Alabama. Workers concede that there is quite a bit of poison ivy in the countryside, but point out that they go for long periods without going out in the woods and getting exposed to it.

Willie Ray Reeves, an employee of Geigy, went to the plant first aid room late in 1969 with his hands broken out in clear blisters. He was referred by management to a skin specialist in Mobile, Alabama. The specialist told Reeves he did not have any idea what caused the trouble, but that he was sure it was not anything in the Geigy plant. His treatment made the condition worse. Reeves finally went to a dermatologist of his own choosing. That doctor told Reeves he was certain that chemical exposure on the job caused the blisters. His treatment was effective toward curing them.

The physician retained by Monsanto Company at Trenton, Michigan, prefers to blame bad personal hygiene on the part of the workers for the frequent rashes which break out among employees in the detergent manufacturing department. Local union officer Adam Caban says, "Every time anyone comes in there with these skin problems the company doctor says he should contact his personal physician. And he tells us that these people have bad hygiene habits. All I can gather from that is that they don't take baths. I don't know. Everyone who works there that I know of showers before he leaves the plant."

Charles Candler of the Monsanto detergent department says the company doctor told him his pimples were caused by something he ate. But Candler and others have gone to dermatologists who tell them the pimples definitely were not caused by diet, but by something contacting their skin.

Union Representative Hugh Owen reports that in the Velsicol Company insecticide plant in Memphis, Tennessee, "We have had cases where management has claimed that the people were on dope—drug addicts. We have had specialists look at them and have had them isolated in hospitals here in Memphis and the doctors report back that the people are not drug addicts. We have had some people that you would call mental cases. The company has felt they were daydreaming. Whether it's the effect from the chemicals out there, we don't know. We have had cases where managers have claimed that people were on the job drunk and it was proven through doctors' statements and through arbitration that they were not drunk, that they were under the influence of fumes of the chemicals."

This plant manufactures nerve-damaging chlorinated hydrocarbon insecticides. There have been cases of men going into convulsions, similar to epileptic seizures, after severe exposures while at work. To suggest that people laboring in such an environment but showing less severe symptoms are drunk or under the influence of narcotics seems somewhat unkind.

Opal Swafford of the Stauffer Chemical Company plant in Chicago Heights, Illinois, has suffered a long time from bronchial asthma which she thinks was caused by exposure to chlorine on the job. She went to the company doctor and, she says, "He told me to drink whiskey and quit smoking cigarets. I asked him if he had ever had bronchial asthma and he said no, but he had treated a lot of it. I had a notion to ask him if he'd ever had a baby."

There are various arrangements by which companies retain doctors. In a few very large plants, full-time medical men are employed. They may have clinics inside the plants and spend more or less full time in them. Medium-sized establishments usually have arrangements with a medical practitioner in the community to come into the plant for a given period each week. Three forenoons weekly is a commonplace schedule. Smaller plants usually make arrangements with a physician or clinic in the neighborhood to send their employees to the doctor's office or clinic when need arises.

Several services are provided by these physicians. Usually they examine applicants for employment, for every company likes to hire new employees of the best available physical condition and the pre-employment medical examination is valuable in compensation cases. They examine and treat employees who report injuries or illnesses. In some cases they certify whether or not an employee is or is not in condition to work and whether his ailment be employment-related or non-occupational. In some cases—too few cases—they give periodic examinations to all employees to determine if they have early symptoms of illness or unusual physical deterioration.

In pre-employment examination, the job applicant is in no position to quarrel with the doctor's findings. In all of the other medical functions listed above, there is frequent occasion for differences of opinion. The sick or injured workman often feels that he is given short shrift when he reports to the company doctor. There are many cases such as those previously cited in which the management-retained physician blames a non-occupational cause for an ailment the employee thinks is job-caused. Rightly or wrongly, workers tend to believe that the company doctors look after company interests first, employee health second.

The M.D. is in a peculiar position. If he tells a worker that his illness is job-caused, the employee may sue the company for workmen's compensation and subpoena the doctor to testify. At best, the typical medical man dislikes appearing on a witness stand. It must be even more difficult when he is put in the position of testifying against the company which has paid his fee. This is a conflict of interest which perhaps would be eliminated by the establishment of socialized medicine. Or, as a more conservative step, a system for paying doctors other than by company check might be devised.

Workers often feel that in the treatment of ailments obviously job-caused they get superficial or discourteous treatment. A man is painfully gassed by chlorine. He gets a penicillin shot and some cough syrup. Perhaps this is all that can be done. The penicillin presumably fights infection which is more likely to occur to damaged than to healthy respiratory tissues. The cough syrup soothes his irritated throat. Still, the man who has suffered the painful and frightening experience of chlorine gassing understandably wants somewhat more tender care.

And there are cases like those of Lewis Scott, who got several teeth knocked out when a crane pulley broke in the U. S. Reduction Company plant in East Chicago, Indiana, on December 27, 1969. He was taken to a nearby hospital at 9:15 a.m. After hours of painful waiting, he finally got attention and got back to the plant at 2 p.m. Vic Kroner, a safety committeeman in the same plant, says, "I've heard two or three fellows already who say they go to the doctor with injuries then wait hours and hours before they get treated." Eugene Owens, a union shop steward in the Humko chemical plant in Memphis, voices the same complaint: "The type of doctor they send you to, you can sign in and he'll send you back in there, sit you on that X-ray table and then leave you there for four hours without even coming in to see about you."

These men refer to fully visible physical injuries. When diagnosis is more difficult, strain between workers and company doctors is even more likely. George D. Shiner, local union vice president, says employees of Glascote Products in Cleveland are not satisfied with the physician who comes into the plant two or three times a week. Shiner says, "I personally never had any problems with him, but I know of men who've gone in there and the doctor told them, 'You're not in pain, you're just acting. There is nothing wrong with you.' One man went in there with something in his eye and the doctor said there was nothing there. The individual went to his own physician, who pulled a piece of steel from his eye, and he brought it back to the company."

Without doubt workers, since they are human like managers, sometimes do malinger, pretend to be hurt when they are not, exaggerate small pains into great ones. But there are countless cases, like the one cited by Shiner, in which examinations by private physicians have found ailments company doctors declared did not exist. The inevitable suspicion, rightly or wrongly, is that company doctors permit the source of their fees to obscure their medical independence. The obvious answer is examination by physicians whose remuneration is from a non-partisan source.

As for periodic physical examinations of workers, a situation of criminal neglect prevails. Industry, the medical profession, state and federal governments, labor unions and everyone else involved should hang their heads in shame. While almost total ignorance prevails about the long-term health effect of tens of thousands of industrial materials, there is proven evidence of chronic injury by some thousands of better-researched materials. Many of these are known to build up in the human body—in bones, in fatty tissue, in blood, in specific organs—with a cumulatively deleterious effect on the body.

There are tests to determine the concentration in the body of many of these dangerous extraneous materials—blood tests, urine tests and fat biopsies, for example. Dr. N. Irving Sax describes a number of these in "Dangerous Properties of Industrial Materials." Chest X-rays and breathing capacity tests can detect various lung ailments in their early stages. It seems obvious that workmen exposed to any toxic or potentially toxic material should have periodic, thorough laboratory tests to detect any accumulation of the material in the body. The man or woman who works in severe dust or fumes which may be lung irritants should have chest X-rays and breathing tests at frequent intervals.

The testimony both of workmen and professionals in the field of medicine reveals that little is being done in the way of periodic examinations. The 1966 report of the U. S. Health, Education and Welfare Department entitled "Protecting the Health of 80 Million Americans" states that 80 percent of the 80 million working Americans "work in places where no type of health service is provided, and the protection given the remaining 20 percent varies from excellent to minimal." A statement by the Occupational Health Committee of Group Health Association of America appended to this same report says that only 2,000 of three million work places in America have medical and health programs established by industry. This statement says that "probably more than half (of the civilian work force) have some degree of physiological impairment which could be greatly reduced if adequate knowledge were available." This means that only one out of each 1,500 work places has a health program. Far fewer than this would have programs including periodic examinations for possible cumulative injuries. The Group Health Association statement was adopted in 1964, but there is utterly no evidence that industrial health service, on balance, has improved since then.

Dr. R. Lomax Wells, testifying on March 5, 1968, before a Congressional committee on behalf of the American Medical Association, said, "Research is badly needed in the development of occupational exposure limits for new chemicals, and physical and biologic agents," and "Rapid detection methods need to be developed for accurate determination of the degree of exposures."

More research and more training of technicians—industrial hygienists, nurses, laboratory technicians and others—has been asked by a long list of professional organizations in the medical field. In one way or another, such recommendations have been made by American Medical Association, American Academy of Occupational Medicine, American Public Health Service, Industrial Medical Association, American Industrial Hygiene Association, American Nurses Association, American Association of Industrial Nurses, and probably other organizations of professional competence.

In spite of these pleas, little is being done to monitor the conditions of human bodies exposed to industrial health hazards. Most of that which is done is superficial. Many men working around such specific poisons as tetraethyl lead (which is added to nearly all gasolines to increase octane ratings) are checked periodically for accumulations. When excessive accumulations appear, the usual company reaction is to transfer the workman to a less exposed part of the plant, either temporarily or permanently. An example of how this works may be found in the Houston Chemical plant in Beaumont, Texas. Harlan Harrison, union chairman there, says, "We're continuously exposed to some part of tetraethyl lead. The company runs a urine sample on us once a month. But in between this time we could all of a sudden go into the red or get highly contaminated with the lead.

"They vent this stuff out into the atmosphere. It falls back to the ground; you can smell it. Some of it doesn't fall right back on us, but goes to other plants around us—Gulf States, particularly, and Mobil Oil which is down below us. Now, the company does take samples, air samples, at Lamar, downtown, and at Gulf States, which is four or five hundred yards from us. But we don't know the results of these and the people there are certainly exposed to this lead whenever we vent it out. What effect it has on you, then or later on, we haven't been able to find out. We have asked these questions. We can't get any answers as of yet."

If, on his monthly check, a man is found to have too much lead in his system, what do they do?

Harrison: "They pull him out of the area. Of course, any

time you are inside that plant or 100 yards from that plant you can still get some contamination, because you can smell it." He recalls two cases of extreme lead poisoning in the plant. In the early 1960's, Sam Stubbs showed severe symptoms and was released from company employment. That was before the union was organized in the plant. In about 1967, Harold Poole, a union committeeman, was "leaded" and was quite ill, with severe weight loss, for several months. As of January, 1970, Harrison says, "He's about back to normal now."

Employees of this plant who go to the company doctor with sickness complaints are examined and told to go to their personal physicans if the ailment is, in the doctor's judgment, non-occupational. He does not tell the employee what he believes to be wrong. However, if the employee has lead poisoning or bromine poisoning, the company doctor insists on treating the case. But, Harrison thinks, "If it's after-effects from lead or something two or three years from now, the company doctor doesn't want to have anything else to do with you."

Harrison is disturbed because the company people will not provide employees any information to take to their personal physicians. "During negotiations in 1969, we asked whether we could see the reports or the employee himself could see his report," says Harrison. "And, also, we asked a breakdown in the numbers that they use in determining how much lead you have in your body or how much you are giving off. They refused at that time to give us any of that information." He adds that the company doctor later told him that if an employee requested information, he (the doctor) "would talk to him about it."

Such vagueness is upsetting. Many workers would like specific, written reports on their examinations, not fatherly "talking to."

In plant after plant, employees testify that they are not told what their own examinations and laboratory tests show. There is an obvious financial incentive for management to maintain secrecy of its knowledge of the individual human being's bodily damage. Knowledge gleaned from these medical records might be used as evidence in demands for workmen's compensation or other financial recompense from the company. Meanwhile, a man can die because of not being forewarned of a deteriorating health condition—a condition that treatment might cure or control. In their secret files, managers thus hold potential keys to life and death—and hope, presumably, that life will overcome whatever physiological harm has been done.

Union negotiating committees frequently ask that such medical records be opened; management with rare exceptions declines. Who should see the records? Filing copies of the records with the union probably would be a violation of medical ethics and the right of the individual to privacy. Copies filed with the individuals well may be lost over the years. Could there be established some sort of neutral, professionally controlled repositories for this information that most likely could save lives and prevent premature disabilities?

The suspicion that company doctors sometimes violate their professional ethics by being less than candid is reinforced by testimony given by distinguished men in the profession. Dr. Hawey A. Wells, director of the Pulmonary Research Laboratory, Conemaugh Valley Memorial Hospital, Johnstown, Pennsylvania, said this to a Congressional committee in 1968:

"Knowledge gained by painful experience in industry is not readily disseminated to the industrial physicians, hygienists and engineers across the country, and in some cases the information is not disseminated at all. There seems to be some tendency to obscure this information, to obstruct the free dissemination of knowledge. It became apparent while we were touring the country with an exhibit that presented the pathology of one particular disease. Many physicians expressed frustrations at having inadequate medical information to diagnose and treat patients with suspected occupational diseases, much less the ability to prevent them.

"Dr. John Zalinsky came up to us in Detroit and told of 30 cases of a chronic lung disease caused by exposure to 'safe'

levels of beryllium dust. He was told by the companies that if
he published this material in the medical literature that he
would have to look for another job. He was torn between
professional honesty and personal security and before he resolved this dilemma he died of his second heart attack. His
material has never been published.

"I have knowledge of a plant that uses manganese, a toxic
material that has been known to be very dangerous for a long
time. Recently, through some bitter experiences, the management of this plant found that it did indeed poison the nervous
system, causing permanent brain damage in exposed workers.
They have used, for about a year, a simple test, no more
complicated than a prick on the finger, that will detect exposure
to this material before permanent nerve injury occurs. How
many hundreds of other companies use manganese but don't
have the advantage of this simple test for detecting exposure
because this test has not been published in this country in the
medical literature?"

Upon questioning by Congressman O'Hara, Dr. Wells
added, "The laboratory that conducts that test has been sworn
to secrecy."

While secrecy of medical records is a problem in those
relatively few plants which process the more deadly and better
known poisons, absence of any examinations at all is the problem in even more. The author asked scores of workers in plants
where there are serious exposures to less toxic dusts and fumes
if they had periodic X-rays or other lung checks. Very few
report thorough examinations. In numerous cases, they say
that once each couple of years or so the company asks the Tuber-
culosis Association to send its mobile X-ray units into the plants.

A poignant case is found in the Carborundum Company
plant in Hickman, Kentucky. The men there are subjected to
extremely bad dust conditions and considerable fume inhalation. While there is no evidence at hand that these particular
dusts and fumes are highly hazardous, it stands to reason that
excessive exposure is not healthful. Some of the dusts are

similar to the coal dusts which cause black lung. The men in Hickman have little health service. There is only one doctor in the town and he is retained by the company. Says Henry Callison, local union president, "The men have no confidence in this doctor. I think he has more interest in outside things. He is a farmer and I think doctoring is more like a sideline or a hobby with him."

When the author suggests, "Well, if I were you I'd take it on myself to get annual physical exams, including chest X-rays," Callison replies, "Well, the wages that we are making are not the highest in the world and physical checkups can be expensive. I am married, have two children, and I can tell you it takes all the money I can scrape to live on."

Callison, one of the higher paid men in the plant, continues, "I know that if I can't afford it—and I don't spend money on carelessness, I don't drink, I know that I take care of my money—and here is this poor guy out there making $2.08 an hour and maybe he has three or four kids. How is he going to do it?"

Aside from the one physician in Hickman, the nearest medical services are in Union City, Tennessee, a town of 12,000 to 14,000 a dozen miles away. Callison believes that to get adequate exams, he likely would have to travel 120 miles to Memphis, which probably would mean lost wages for traveling time as well as medical fees.

Many workers believe that employers should be responsible for the full costs of periodic medical examinations, especially when there are health-hazardous working conditions. The more callous employers respond to this suggestion with a "take it or leave it attitude," suggesting that the noise, dust, fumes or other sickening things are a foreknown condition of work for which the men are paid by the hour. The individual, they suggest, has the full freedom to decline employment. Employers who are more gentle-tongued insist that they are doing all they can to protect employee health, but that it is not fair for their companies to assume full financial responsibility for health services when conditions in the work place often are not the cause of sickness.

This is an interesting conflict of views. Does it suggest that the entire matter of preserving life and health be moved into neutral hands, or into some system subject to bipartisan labor-management administration?

12

The Statistics Lie

To counter the assertion that industrial workers suffer from serious and extensive health damage, managers cite statistics purporting to show that relatively few deaths and injuries occur during hours of employment. In testimony before legislative committees and in speeches before public forums, they consistently assert that men and women are safer at work than at home or while driving or riding in automobiles. Particularly they quote highway death totals and relate them to the occupational death tallies.

It is an invidious and pointless comparison. What does it accomplish? Are we not, each of us, diminished by any death, by any hurt? To cite the injuries of the road does not justify the injuries occurring in other places.

But even though the comparison of auto deaths versus work deaths is irrelevant, let us examine it and its distortions. The formal statistics show that approximately 14,500 people are killed annually in the United States by occupational accidents, compared with approximately 50,000 who die annually in automobile wrecks. About 80 million Americans work, while about 200 million, counting children, ride in cars. It would appear that only one of each 5,714 workers is killed on the job each year while one of each 4,000 automobile passengers is killed annually.

But every motor vehicle accident death is recorded through the nation's extensive network of police forces, while occupational death ordinarily is entered into the statistics only if the individual dies while at work or while under treatment for a traumatic accident which happened on the job before witnesses. The death caused directly but less visibly by health damage rarely, if ever, is counted.

The disabling injuries actually recorded for 80 million workers exceed those of 200 million automobile passengers. Reported temporarily disabling work injuries in the United States are on the order of 2.2 million each year, or almost one for every 36 workers. Automobile accidents cause 1.9 million temporarily disabling injuries annually, or one for every 105 people who ride in cars. Again, sicknesses caused by work conditions are rarely, if ever, counted. No one knows how many of these there are, for neither medical research nor statistical records touch more than the bare edge of the occupational health situation.

Even the records on immediate, highly visible injuries are grossly falsified. Men suffer broken arms, broken legs and other serious hurts which are not reported to record-keeping agencies. Various states have various rules pertaining to the reporting of accidents at work—and there are varying degrees of enforcement of the laws. In some states, the employer is supposed to report even a cut finger which removes the worker from his job only long enough for the application of a small bandage. Are all these reported?

The National Safety Council defines a "lost-time" accident as one which so injures a worker as to prevent him or her from performing normally assigned duties. A nick on a finger might incapacitate, for practical purposes, a woman assigned to delicate assembly of tiny parts in an electronic device, yet she might work efficiently while wearing a lower leg cast. There are few industrial jobs that can be performed by a man on crutches, yet every day men are brought into industrial plants on crutches and assigned to make-work chores or no work at all so that they will not be counted as having suffered lost-time accidents.

Eugene Charles, local union president in the U. S. Reduction Company plant in East Chicago, says, "We have men every now and then hobbling around there on crutches, one arm in a sling, anything, just doing nothing, just sitting in the locker room."

As of January 17, 1970, the safety sign in the Rohm & Haas chemical plant at Pasadena, Texas, said that the plant had recorded 458 consecutive days without a lost-time accident. Asked if he thought the figure was distorted, union workmen's committeeman Bob Walter says, "Very much so. We've had the problem of people getting burns from steam hoses and so on and so forth and they haul them in there on crutches. When I first went to work out there I got a skin irritation from benzene. My hands swelled up. Oh, they were huge! Well, they brought me back out there and sat me at the desk in front of the telephone and asked me to answer the phone for, I guess, about two weeks to keep from listing a lost-time accident. Well, this happens. They'll bring the people back in on stretchers if they have to."

Francisco Montalvo, local union president, reports that in the Stauffer Chemical Company plant in Chicago Heights, Illinois, employees "frequently, very frequently" are asked to work even though they cannot perform normal duties. "In 95 percent of the cases," says Montalvo, "the employee is asked to come back within 24 hours. When they can't even walk, they'll bring them in the station wagon. This is why they were able to go up to five million hours without a lost-time accident that one time. But recently some of the employees have refused to come in and this is why the record shows that lost-time accidents happened more frequently this past year than before."

Roy Barnes, local union president representing employees of Shell Oil and Shell Chemical at Pasadena, Texas, says, "I know that on occasion they have brought people with broken feet out on crutches and set them down in an office in order to maintain their no-lost-time safety records. Their safety records are a joke. They don't report accidents."

Johnny Cicero, local union president in the DuPont plant at Watson, Alabama, comments on the matter of bringing injured men to work: "They are bad about this. I think all companies are. They want to get a man back in the plant, not necessarily to work but just to get him back on the job. They put him in an office—you know, set him down, a man not expected to do anything. It looks good on paper, but it's no good, actually."

There are incentives, human and financial, for such falsification of injury reports. The plant safety director wants to make a good record. It looks good to the company headquarters officials who decide on promotions and salary increases. The home office authorities do not know—and probably do not care to know—if a man who should be home in bed is lying in pain on a locker room bench. The plant manager wants to make a good impression on the home office and the general public. A nice little article and picture in the local newspaper likely follows when a plaque celebrating a long period without accidents is presented by National Safety Council or some other organization.

The financial incentive is based on insurance rates, including workmen's compensation premium charges, which vary depending on the number of claims paid in the particular plant. A few accidents reported can cause insurance rate increases which may be more costly than the payment of several days wages to workers who are non-productive.

Many managers will represent that they bring an injured man to work out of sheer generosity. The employee draws full pay while doing little or nothing, whereas he could be home drawing a lesser income in workmen's compensation payments or other forms of insurance. This financial difference to the worker sometimes prevails, sometimes it does not. Most union contracts provide full pay for a stipulated period for men disabled by job injuries. Those which do not should do so; a person hurt in line of duty should receive full pay until he is able to work again.

All things being considered, direct financial incentives probably are less of a factor than the maintenance of a good appearance. Public relations has been carried to the point of absurdity in America. Making the good record, maintaining the good image, too often has overshadowed the substance of actually doing things right. Perhaps it is this hypocrisy which has caused rebellious youth to make such a fetish of spurning good appearance, of deliberately affecting shabbiness and poor grooming.

The charges by workers that their employers falsify accident records are substantiated by people with broader overviews of the situation. George Taylor, safety director of the AFL-CIO, told a 1969 conference sponsored by AFL-CIO's Industrial Union Department:

"It is my opinion and it is shared by others that if there were adequate reporting of occupational injuries and illnesses, the present statistical picture, shocking as it is, would be twice as bad. Although there is standardized reporting of wages, productivity, various other economic and social indices—not to mention war casualties and bomb tonnage—no one has gotten around to establishing adequate and standardized reporting of the casualties suffered by America's workers on the job. Likewise, no one has figured out what it really means to a casualty victim in terms of what happens to his family, its finances, its hopes and plans and its long-term security."

Ralph Nader, the attorney and author who has become America's foremost crusader for safety, told a U. S. Senate committee June 28, 1968, that "there is conscious underreporting of data by American industry." He testified, "The underreporting takes basically two forms. One is by influencing the definitional content of what constitutes an injury they can affect the reporting of injuries. The definition of injury is under the umbrella of the United States Standards Institute of America, so-called, formerly the American Standards Association, a private agency composed largely of trade associations and dominated by them. USSIA has the definition of work injury pretty much to itself in the United States.

"The second technique of underreporting is more willful; it involves, in effect, going to almost any lengths to reduce the recording of lost work time, to even keep the accident-level reporting in the plant down. This takes one form after an injury, of putting a worker in some other area of the plant just as long as he checks in so there is no lost time recorded.

"The data also are underestimated by the virtue of the lack of sufficient investigation in the area of occupational health injuries. These are the so-called cumulative kills, the insidious, silent encroachment on men's health which can be determined in a laboratory, which can be determined clinically, such as carbon monoxide and lead exposure. But there has not been a sufficient structure of data collection that will determine the morbidity and shortening of life and other forms of disability for the working man. Everybody knows in this field that this is a very serious problem. In fact, some of the worst aspects of this problem in American industry are described almost furtively in a kind of whisper by men, who are well-intentioned men, but fear the consequences of speaking out."

Dr. Miriam Sachs, Director of Comprehensive Health Planning of the New Jersey State Department of Health, told a U. S. House committee February 28, 1968, that data are needed about four fields—statistics of industrial accidents, statistics on the evidence of occupational disease, data on the extent of exposure of workers to occupational hazards and statistics of differential mortality and morbidity by income group and occupation. "In none of these fields do available data approximate adequacy," said Dr. Sachs.

In testimony June 19, 1968, Dr. Philip R. Lee, assistant secretary of the Department of Health, Education and Welfare, told a Senate committee that it was known that more than 300,000 workers are totally disabled each year as a result of occupational diseases. He added, "The precise toll of occupational illness, however, is not known. Several factors, which include inadequate reporting, shield the extent of occupational illness from the view of medical and safety experts, the public, responsible leaders in industry and labor, and particularly from the victims."

Dr. John J. Hanlon, speaking as president of the American Public Health Association, said in Congressional testimony on March 11, 1968, "We simply have nothing approaching a good reporting system and until we do we must agree with Secretary Wirtz, who told this committee, 'Our present statistics are too weak for any meaningful purpose.'"

When distinguished professionals concerned with occupational health testify that there is underreporting of accidents and illnesses, or that they are forced to grope in a dark world of unknowns while they seek prevention or cure, their words are intellectually impressive but terribly generalized and impersonal.

Those men and women who, in Ralph Nader's words, "are dying silently" are more explicit and personal as they describe the actual conditions where they work.

Samuel Austin tells how it felt in the Stauffer plant in Chicago Heights after he hurt his back: "This Monday on the way home I was in so much pain I couldn't drive my car. So I got out of my car and a highway patrolman saw me and came over and asked me what was wrong. He drove me home and told me he'd better not catch me in a car again. So Tuesday management sent the station wagon to pick me up and I stayed in the locker room. I couldn't sit very long and I couldn't lie down very long in one position. They would send the janitor out every couple of hours to see how I was doing, to help turn me over."

No lost time.

13

Very Little Law and Order

"It is patently impossible for the worker to take responsibility for his own health and safety in a complex world of physical and chemical hazards which are little understood even by experts and which are clearly beyond his control." So said Charles C. Johnson, Jr., administrator of consumer protection and environmental health services for the U. S. Department of Health, Education and Welfare, in an address in 1969 to a conference sponsored by the Industrial Union Department of AFL-CIO.

"The fact is," Johnson added, "that man has created a new environment but he has not created a new man. We are the products of a slow evolutionary process, and we still have the same physical characteristics that our caveman ancestors had. We still need clean air to breathe and clean water to drink; we are still helpless against unseen or uncontrollable hazards in the environment. We have developed no second sight that tells us when an invisible beam or a seemingly harmless vapor is doing insidious damage to our health."

As for the individual workman's responsibility for taking care of himself, Johnson said: "Certainly every worker needs to be made aware of the hazards he confronts in the workplace and educated to exercise caution—to 'watch his step,' to wear earplugs and a hard hat and safety shoes when required . . . But what we can do—and must do—is to create a working environment in which such a person, exercising reasonable care, can be assured that sudden death or the slow process of industrial disease will not be the wages of his work."

If, as Johnson suggests, the workman cannot by his own actions fully protect himself while on the job, who then must do so or cooperate with the worker in doing so? Management spokesmen say that they are concerned, that they are doing everything possible, and that they assume full responsibility for health and safety. The working people quoted in this report disagree, saying that management generally is not maintaining healthful and safe conditions.

With this difference of opinion prevailing, there seems to be a clear demand for participation by neutral forces—presumably government agencies. Debate on this proposition was brought into full focus in January, 1968, when President Lyndon B. Johnson proposed to the U. S. Congress the enactment of comprehensive health and safety legislation covering all workers in interstate commerce. It was the first substantial Presidential demand for action in this field since December, 1910, when President William Howard Taft asked Congress to put a stop to the "frightful diseases" resulting from the manufacture of matches with phosphorus. (There were brief, passing references to occupational health and safety in messages transmitted by President Truman and President Eisenhower).

Such governmental inspection, rule-making and enforcement as now exist rest mostly with the states. Theoretically 36 million out of 80 million workers in the U. S. A. have some measure of Federal protection, but practically speaking this does not amount to much. A third of a million of these are in the maritime industry and are covered by special laws. Nearly three million are civilian Federal employees. Twenty-seven million are affected by the Public Contracts Act (commonly known as the Walsh-Healey Act) and six million are covered by the Service Contracts Act.

The Walsh-Healey Act provides that private entrepreneurs performing contracts for, or selling goods to, the Federal government must meet certain minimum standards in wages and working conditions. The principal application of this law has

been to make sure that such employers pay wages equivalent
to the prevailing rates in the industry or the region.

In recent years, under the general umbrella of "working
conditions," the Department of Labor has issued safety codes
of generalized and limited nature and has ordered that government contractors conform to them. This has been no great leap
forward. David Swankin, director of the Bureau of Labor
Standards, told an AFL-CIO Industrial Union Department conference in 1969:

"The Public Contracts Act covers perhaps 27 million employees working in some 75,000 plants holding government
contracts valued at some $37 billion. Because our investigative
resources are small, we inspect less than three percent of the
covered plants each year. It is obviously necessary to be se-
lective, to pick the ones likely to involve the most hazards.
Our initial inspections . . . indicate that about 90 percent
of the companies are in violation of one or more provisions
of the Walsh-Healey safety and health regulations. Nor are
these companies by any means small, fly-by-night operations. . . .
One plant found recently with over 200 violations was a
branch plant of an industrial giant with an excellent safety
record, one of the nation's leaders. It had both a safety program and a staff."

Such minimal inspections are frustrating to working people
and their unions as they grope for means of eliminating health
and safety hazards. But lacking other means of bringing outside pressure to bear on their employers, numerous locals of
Oil, Chemical and Atomic Workers Union in recent years
have filed health and safety complaints with the Department of
Labor under the Walsh-Healey provisions. Sometimes these
complaints result in inspections, sometimes they do not.

When investigations are made, results often are intangible.
After the serious fire and explosion in the Shell Chemical Company plant at Pasadena, Texas, in 1968, the union asked for a
Walsh-Healey inspection. An investigator did come into the
plant. He wrote a report on his findings. The union asked

for a copy, but the government declined to release it on the ground that parts of the report were either hearsay or were opinions which investigators promised would be kept confidential.

Subsequently, the union joined with associates of Ralph Nader in a lawsuit demanding of the government that it permit access to this record and to certain other safety inspection records. The suit is based on the 1967 Public Information Act, which supposedly makes available to the public a wide range of government records which do not affect national security.

Workers, acting individually or in concert through their unions, face a stacked deck in most cases of safety inspections by state or federal authorities. The managers get a copy of the investigative reports, the workers whose lives and health are affected do not. This is as unfair as to deny a transcript of a trial record to one litigant to a lawsuit while giving it to the other side for appeals purposes. There remains deeply imbedded in American law and law enforcement practices a prejudice for property as against people.

In several other respects, workers seeking health and safety improvements contend with what amounts to industry-government collusion. Unions or individual workmen file requests for safety inspections. More often than not, inspectors responding to these petitions contact managers only, by-passing the very individuals or organizations which have made the complaints. Frequently, they make appointments for inspection tours several days in advance with company officials, thus giving the managers time to correct the hazardous conditions complained of. It is as if a policeman with search warrant in hand should telephone ahead to a suspect and say, "We're coming to your place day after tomorrow to see if you have any heroin on the premises."

Under guidance of managers, inspectors often are shepherded to the cleanest and safest sections of the plants and steered away from more hazardous areas. Often, having advance notice, managers change operational procedures or entirely close down production units of hazardous nature. Usually it is only by hearsay that the workers are aware if an inspection has been made and usually they are not told the specific results.

Sometimes it is only by chance that workers or union officers have an opportunity to contribute to inspections. An example that would be amusing if it were not so serious is related by Lawrence Scafuro, local union president, concerning an inspection made of the metals reduction plant of Reactive Metals, Incorporated, in Ashtabula, Ohio. Late in 1969, the local filed a Walsh-Healey complaint about health hazards, especially excessive dust conditions. Union officers heard no more about it. Then one day early in 1970 the plant was put into immaculate condition because some people from the Pratt-Whitney Company, which uses titanium produced there, were visiting the establishment.

Watching these visitors go through, Scafuro noticed one stranger tagging along who did not seem to be a member of the Pratt-Whitney group. Suspecting that this man might be a Walsh-Healey inspector, Scafuro approached the stranger and said, "We really got a good shafting today." The visitor asked why and Scafuro said, "They cleaned up the plant for the Pratt-Whitney people. I wish you would return at 7:30 tonight."

In response to Scafuro's hint, the stranger reversed his direction of travel through the plant. The company safety man attempted to ease the visitor back on the route of the directed tour, but the stranger persisted in back-tracking.

Scafuro relates, "He started up in a tower, where all this stuff is crushed. He got half way up the tower and he had to turn back. It was so dusty and filthy that he could go no farther. He had to go back to where people were chipping and they had just dumped a pot of titanium sponge. They jammed the crusher and everything got fouled up. What a mess he walked into then! This Walsh-Healey man was running for his instruments and stuff and checking the lines. There wasn't enough suction in these lines. I think he just had a field day by reversing his path in the plant."

Unfortunately, it is not often that a union officer has an opportunity to provide this sort of guidance to an inspector.

Nearly all management spokesmen object to expansion of the trivial measure of Federal protection now extended to working people on matters of occupational health and safety. Witness after witness for trade associations has paraded before Congress since President Johnson posed the issue in 1968. These management witnesses consistently urge that the matter be left in the hands of the 50 states. Some refer to "industry-state" partnership, a suggestion of dubious value since many of the large corporations are richer and stronger than many of the states and in view of the fact that the states have made a dismal record.

The 50 states employ a total of about 1,600 occupational health and safety inspectors and the Federal government employs fewer than 100. Of the 1,600 state inspectors, a large percentage are steam boiler and elevator inspectors who do not apply their time to modern health and safety hazards. But even if we take a generous view and say that all these 1,700 inspectors work all the time checking conditions, and even if we say that their ranks may have edged upward to 2,000 in number by the time these words are in print, we see that there can be little real surveillance of three million places of employment. We still find that there is little enforcement of America's very limited laws pertaining to job safety and health.

In 1968, the AFL-CIO News sent a questionnaire to the labor bodies in all states asking each to report how many occupational safety inspectors and how many game and fish wardens each state employed. Replies from 25 states revealed 985 safety inspectors as compared to 2,580 game and fish wardens. Protection of wildlife certainly is laudable in this age of shrinking wilderness and ecological imbalance, but it would seem that people, too, are entitled to safeguards.

Even these few inspectors do little in the field of occupa-

tional health. Dr. William H. Stewart, Surgeon General of
the United States, told a House committee on February 20,
1968, "The greatest barrier to the control of known occupational
hazards and occupationally caused disease is the lack of trained
personnel for correcting workplace hazards. Illinois, the third
largest of industrial states, has only three industrial hygienists
for the entire state."

Dr. Stewart at that time said, "As far as the states go, there
are a few states that have (occupational health) programs but
in general, if one wants to generalize, the efforts of the states
are very weak. For example, there are only 26 states with any
programs, and they have 146 employees in this effort. There
are probably eight states which are doing as good a job as they
can within the restrictions of budget and personnel that they
have."

Dr. Stewart later submitted to the committee a list of nine
states which he labeled as having good occupational health programs. One of these was New Jersey. At that time New Jersey
had one of the largest occupational safety staffs in the nation—
127 inspectors and 48 engineers. Yet, according to Dr. Miriam
Sachs of New Jersey's Department of Health, the state then
had only 11 employees in the field of occupational health.

In both health and safety fields, union workers tell of frustration in their efforts to secure state assistance. Several times
when the author asked them about requesting state inspectors,
the men simply laughed sourly at what they considered a very
foolish question.

The few health and safety inspectors on state payrolls
work under restrictive laws. A specific example is found in
Kansas. On November 5, 1968, local union President Ray
Lovelady wrote to Robert Borchardt, the Kansas Labor Department's director of safety, asking an investigation of two recent
deaths in the Phillips refinery in Kansas City, and requesting
that he as a union officer be contacted at the time of the
investigation.

Hearing no response, Lovelady wrote again on December

18. Under date of December 27, he got an answer from Delno Bass, Kansas labor commissioner, who told Lovelady that an inspection had been made on November 8 by Harris Reeves, industrial inspector. "Mr. Reeves requested an employee representative be present during the investigation and was refused," said Bass. The refusal came from the company. Bass advised Lovelady in general terms that Inspector Reeves had found half a dozen unsafe practices in the plant, but Bass could not give the union officer the specific findings.

Said Bass: "The statutes specify a working relationship between this department and company management . . . and do not include providing information to a third party." He also said, "This agency, as does all other state agencies, operates within certain areas of authority and responsibility as defined by statute. I would suggest you contact your representatives and senators and present your view on needed changes or additions to the laws, rules and regulations."

The contacting of senators and representatives, both Federal and state, is something the union certainly is taking up. It is shocking that a law provides that information be given only to the party accused, and not to the representatives of the injured parties. The injured parties in this case were Floyd Halsell and Howard Thomas. Both of them had been killed in that Phillips refinery, in separate accidents, shortly before their union president wrote his complaint to the state.

Texas has a weak industrial safety law which declares that it is "a crime against the state" for personnel of the state agency enforcing the law to reveal any information that might infringe on company secrets. This is not a threat of civil damage claims, mind you, but "a crime against the state" and criminal penalties are specified. Any inspector or administrator is inhibited from reporting anything he has seen in a plant for fear he might inadvertently reveal a process secret.

Charles Johnson, union safety chairman in the Montrose chemical plant in Newark, tells his view of New Jersey's state inspections: "In April or May of 1969, we had an accident with cyanide. Two men we thought were exposed were treated on the job. I saw Brother Ray (Ray Rogowski, union district director) and he called up the state immediately. The state sends an inspector down to our place. He doesn't see the union man. He doesn't say anything. Only thing I get from him is through the company. Now, the company can change it and switch it the way they want it. He never said anything to any union officer or employee. They didn't recognize the union at all."

And, says J. W. Carpenter, local union president in the Geigy Chemical Company plant in McIntosh, Alabama: "You can almost tell without talking to anyone when you're going to have a state inspection because everything is cut down to, say, half rate. Everything is cleaned up. One thing that gets real comical, that the formulators make a joke out of: they shut formulations completely down, dust everything off; they post a man at each end of the warehouse and then when the inspector starts his way they run and crank up everything where the machinery is running and there's no dust whatsoever around. I have observed this myself. I'm not speaking from hearsay."

The union in the Reactive Metals, Incorporated, sodium plant in Ashtabula, Ohio, has not asked for state safety inspections, but local union President Charles Thomas says: "There have been occasions when there has been a state man coming in to look through the plant. We're told the hour he is coming, and we pull this tickler, we call it, off the gas line. None of this work is to be done in these hours that your inspector is to be around. This is holding down all smoke in the shop, all gas, none of the work is to be done at this time that normally would be."

Anthony Pinelli, union safety committeeman in the same plant, adds, "We were told Tuesday of this past week inspectors were coming into this area. And that particular day when the inspectors came there was nothing being discharged in the air. They just lowered the production on the furnaces where there was just a nil amount of what you call emission in the air."

All ex-soldiers recall with chuckles the preparations made in military installations for visits from high brass. With ample advance notice, camp commanders would clean everything up. The same ridiculous sort of so-called "inspections" are made by home office personnel of their far-flung industrial plants. Many members testify to having been ordered to work overtime in preparation for well-heralded visits by corporate officers.

An example is given by Francisco Montalvo, local union president in the Stauffer Chemical Company plant in Chicago Heights: "Certain departments that might be dusted too much or polluting the air too much or the sewers too much, these departments are shut down temporarily to clean out for repairs, or in maintenance we're made to do something to this or that to get it running again. Everybody works 16 hours a day to get everything cleaned up so it looks spic-and-span for the big heads. There are some departments that are hard to get clean and they just shut them down for the two or three days that the big wheels are coming in, so that they can see something clean."

Ernie Baxter, a fellow worker, adds: "Once every year they have this inter-plant safety contest, supposedly safety contest. They go around from plant to plant with inspection committees and look the properties over. Well, once a year we have a big clean-up over here. They clean up everything so that it's half way decent, as well as painting the plant. The day after the inspection you can't tell the place has been touched."

In the Army there is one back-stop, at least, for the prettied-up formal inspections which prove nothing. Complaints may be lodged with the Inspector General. He can send investigating officers into a military installation without notice to the installation's own officers.

There can be no effective governmental regulation of industrial health and safety conditions unless government inspectors have the legal power and the administrative will to make surprise inspections. And there must be enough of these inspectors to make reasonably frequent inspections, just as there must be sufficient policemen to patrol the streets and highways.

Aside from whether these policemen issue many traffic tickets or make many arrests, the very presence of their marked cars cruising along the roads has a cautionary effect on motorists.

It is said that morals cannot be legislated. No doubt this is true as regards personal morals, but the strong arm of the law can reinforce morals insofar as public conduct is concerned. The vast majority of people adhere to the precept that it is wrong to murder or to steal. Nevertheless, society has found it necessary also to pass laws forbidding these acts—and even lesser transgressions such as making too much noise or spitting on the sidewalk.

Legislation proposed in Congress, and from time to time in the various states, would regulate by law the conduct of managers as this conduct affects the health and safety of workers. Are such regulations unreasonable? Most management spokesmen appearing before Congress say that they are. They complain that they would be hounded and heckled by unqualified inspectors. Essentially, they take the view that what goes on inside the industrial plants is private business, although most of them more or less contradict themselves by urging that the states, not the Federal government, be charged with whatever regulation is imposed. They urge that each state set standards, rather than that there be national standards of health and safety. This would create a duplication of effort both wasteful and inefficient. Presumably people in Michigan know more about automobile manufacture than those of any other state, yet the same hazards would exist in Missouri's three or four automobile assembly plants. Texas has more oil refineries than any other state, while North Dakota has only one refinery presenting essentially the same hazards. It would seem obvious that application of the national wisdom would be more feasible than asking each state to draw up its own codes covering each industry.

Petroleum industry lobbyists weep copious tears about the troubles they would suffer if inspected by what they call unqualified people. Admittedly, oil refining is a highly sophisticated industry and its major dangers can be detected best by trained engineers. But such engineers could be employed. Anyway, it would take no expert to note the lighting—a simple and cheap thing to correct—is inadequate in a repair shop in the Rock Island refinery in Zionsville, Indiana.

Some management spokesmen say it would cost the taxpayers too much to provide governmental regulation of health and safety. William E. Naumann, speaking for the Associated General Contractors of America, told a U. S. House committee in 1968 that it has been estimated that enforcement of a proposed bill before Congress would require 11,459 inspectors, 1,149 supervisors and 3,800 clerks.

Numbers are what one makes of them. This force of 16,408 would be equivalent to about one Army division, although its equipment would be far less expensive than that of the troops. It would amount to about one governmental employee for each 5,000 workers. If the average employee of the government agency, from supervisor through clerks, should cost $15,000 per year, that would be $3 per year per employee protected.

Again and again we find ourselves playing the numbers game, applying the economic yardstick to every consideration. This is wrong. The values of life and health, inexpressible in dollars, should be entered into the equation.

Certain government spokesmen urging the passage of health and safety legislation justify it on economic grounds. HEW's 1966 report, "Protecting the Health of Eighty Million Americans," notes that these 80 million workers represent 40 percent of the nation's population and pay 60 percent of the taxes. If the health of these people could be improved so that they would be absent from work just one-fifth less, says the report, there would be a $10 billion increase in the gross national product.

Senator Ralph Yarborough said in a Senate committee hearing in 1968 that he had seen figures indicating that work accidents and illnesses alone cost the American economy $6.8 billion each year. Ralph Nader sardonically responded to the senator that this really might not be a quantitative drain on the economy. He said that "when workers are injured, and so forth, they generally make demand for medical services and other services, which constitute a sub-economy, and it is not really in the overall sense a quantitative drain on the economy. It may be a qualitative drain, in terms of that isn't what we want to spend part of our economy doing. We would rather do something more progressive than repairing broken bones, if we can avoid the breaking of bones."

Nader made the point that workers might, involuntarily, be spending the six billion dollars or so each year on medical services. He implied that perhaps the workers would prefer to juice up the economy by working more regularly and spending their dollars on something else.

On another occasion, speaking before the 1969 AFL-CIO Industrial Union Department health and safety conference, Senator Yarborough spoke of both money and pain. "I have represented (in law practice) the widows of killed workmen and there is nothing more tragic in a lawyer's office to see than the drawn face of that widow with those little children when she realizes that in place of this able-bodied strong worker, earning a good wage or salary, she has got to try to exist on this pittance of workmen's compensation and try to educate her family and get by. They are pittances . . . It is cheaper to let a man get hurt than to have a decent standard."

Gamesmanship with numbers misses the point. The protection of the bodies of the 80 million men and women who work is a matter of right, not economics. It is a matter of order and justice and it should be a matter of law.

In the general regulation of society, laws are passed to protect both economic goods and the bodies and the dignity of people. We employ policemen to prevent theft and to apprehend thieves—a purely economic matter, for thievery ordinarily does not cause physical pain. We employ policemen to prevent murder and apprehend murderers. Murder is an economic crime in that it halts the productivity of a person—a productivity that sometimes can be measured in dollars—and it also is a non-economic crime in that it destroys a life of a value that cannot be calculated. And we employ policemen to prevent rape and apprehend rapists, even though rape has no economic significance whatsoever. We oppose this crime because it is an abhorrent insult to the human body and human dignity.

We should employ law enforcement officers to police occupational health and safety conditions for both economic and humanitarian reasons, with emphasis on the humanitarian aspect. Some industrial working conditions, such as working in excessive dust, are an affront to human dignity even when not probably injurious to health. They should not be tolerated in a civilized society.

This is *not* to suggest that those who manage industry are the equivalent of thieves, murderers or rapists. They are, in some cases, the equivalent of the fellow who, in hot pursuit of a sale and a commission, drives too fast and risks causing death on the roadway. Policing of the managers is in order, although policing alone will not correct the situation.

14

Collective Bargaining for Health

Three distinct forces—management, labor unions and the public through its government—have roles to play in protecting the health and safety of workers. No one of these alone can do the job. No combination of two can achieve fully effective results. The participation of all three is needed.

Management efforts, subject thus far only to limited prodding from unions and government, have been inadequate. Self-policing is contrary to the incentives of the profit system and contrary to human nature.

Some think the whole matter should be turned over to government as a supposedly neutral force. Few labor unionists have confidence in state governments, but many think that the police power of Federal government is great enough and incorruptible enough to be effective. That is not necessarily so, for the record shows that government agencies charged with regulating business often have become more the servants than the masters of those they are supposed to oversee. Conspicuous examples are the Interstate Commerce Commission and the Federal Power Commission. Such agencies are supposed to protect consumers, but consumers have no effective representation in the agency staffs and before agency hearings. Whenever the private citizen hears references to "industry-government partnership," he is well advised to put his women and children in a safe place, grab his gun and man the barricades.

The fact is that the American system is an adversary system. None in it, except perhaps for a few cloistered clerics and scholars, survive by following the torches of pure truth and objectivity. Attorneys on opposing sides of a lawsuit do not pretend to present the whole truth; each lawyer piles up arguments and evidence for his client only while conveniently remaining silent on all points that might help the other side. The hope is that neutral judge and jury will find justice somewhere between the half-truths presented by the opposing litigants. So it is in virtually all affairs. One works for his own interests. The most ethical of men avoid lies, telling the truth, but not necessarily the whole truth. They leave it to the countervailing forces to tell the rest of the truth—if they are sharp enough.

Under this adversary system, government regulation of health and safety conditions can be effective only if there is a force which aggressively presents the workers' views. Management certainly will resist regulations, for many of these will be contrary to economic interests of management and annoying to the human individuals who are managers.

Can labor and management jointly police conditions without participation by government? Theoretically, yes, there might be a situation in which government police powers would not be needed. In such case, the government should play a major role in research and standards setting even if not in the enforcement of standards.

Practically speaking, it is unlikely that unions will be able to negotiate fully satisfactory conditions. Probably government enforcement powers will be needed on at least a standby basis for use when labor-management negotiations are inadequate. At any rate, it is the inherent right and duty of government to protect its citizens, wherever they may be, including inside the work places. Government should not waive this responsibility.

There can be substantial, even dramatic, progress made through union-management negotiations and cooperation if unions will apply themselves to the task and managers will share the responsibility with unions. Such progress will lessen the need for government interference. An ideal situation might be one in which government holds strong powers, but seldom finds it necessary to use them because union-management efforts have minimized the need for them. In such case, no doubt the government could carry on enforcement with far fewer than the 16,000 inspectors, supervisors and clerks some observers estimate as being the current need.

At present, union-management health and safety efforts are fully effective in few industrial installations. In those few cases, there appears to be either extraordinary concern on the part of the union members backed by militancy of union attitudes, or extraordinary cooperativeness on the part of management, or both.

There likely are other examples, but the author has encountered only one local of Oil, Chemical and Atomic Workers whose members appear convinced that their joint union-management safety committee has achieved conditions as safe as can be expected.

In the home plant of Carborundum Company in Niagara Falls, New York, where about 3,000 people work and the union membership is militant, there has been since 1948 a clause in the union contract providing for a labor-management safety committee and unusually good leadership has appeared in the committee. This committee began with limited strength, but has grown over 22 years into an effective force. It consists of three members from the union, three from management. The union's own safety committee consists of 11 members. Both groups meet punctually once each month.

In each department of the plant, 56 in all, there is a safety monitor appointed by management subject to union approval. This probably is as good a procedure as any for securing fair-minded safety men. Any employee has the right to refuse work he considers hazardous. If he thinks a machine or a procedure is unsafe, he tells his supervisor. If the supervisor agrees, he locks the machine out of operation, attaches a warning "do not operate" tag, and summons a mechanic to make necessary repairs. When the individual employee is satisfied that the danger has been eliminated, he proceeds with his work.

If the supervisor does not agree to take the machine out of operation in the first place, or if there is disagreement after repairs are made as to whether the machine is safe, the employee contacts his departmental safety man, who passes the word to the front office. The situation is then evaluated by a committee consisting of the local union's safety chairman and two management people. Management has a two-to-one edge in the decision making, but Stanley Kasprzak, union safety chairman since 1958, says that in almost every case there have been unanimous decisions. In the very few cases where the management men out-vote Kasprzak, he can file a grievance for consideration by plant management and potential arbitration. Meanwhile, the machine stays out of operation. This is an unusual power on the part of a union, an unusual concession on the part of management.

The Carborundum plant manufactures a wide variety of abrasives—grinding wheels, sandpapers, emory cloth, whetstones and the like. The processes involve crushing of extraordinarily hard solid materials to produce the abrasive grits, with resultant dangers of bad dust conditions. Dusts present the greatest potential problem in the factory, but according to Kasprzak they are kept well under control. When employees in a department think dust is too thick, they simply walk out until the condition is corrected. Dust monitoring is carried on by management with union participation and all test findings are given to the union which has the option of sending the findings out to such agencies as the New York Department of Labor for analysis, and has done so on occasion.

Each employee participates in a departmental safety training meeting each month.

Kasprzak is convinced that while dust may at times be annoying, it is kept within limits not hazardous to health. In the 12 years he has served as safety chairman, he is aware of only one employee having been hospitalized with lung spots that might have come from work conditions.

Kasprzak, who attends annual National Safety Council

meetings and talks with union men from many other companies and industries, believes his local has the best safety program of any local union in the United States. Yet in another facility of this same company, a smaller, relatively new Carborundum Company plant at Hickman, Kentucky, safety conditions are bad and the company stubbornly refuses to permit establishment of a labor-management committee or to grant employees the right to refuse to perform work they consider unsafe.

The excellent health and safety program in the Niagara Falls plant well can be copied by many other unions, but in some circumstances this pattern might be hard to follow. Operations there are pretty much on the batch basis, as contrasted to the continuous-flow processes often used when liquid products are handled. There is less interlocking of various plant operations. The shutdown of one machine or one department is easier for management to tolerate because the remainder of the equipment usually can continue operating. The long-organized local union is more militant than most, with an extraordinary sense of unity among the members—anyone who gets into dispute with one member likely has the entire membership to fight. Management apparently accepts this reality and makes more than usual efforts to avoid antagonizing the work force.

Leadership is another factor. Some locals seem to have it in plentiful supply, others have little. The law of averages does not seem to prevail in this matter. The Niagara Falls local has many able leaders.

Kasprzak is an unusual man. A soft-spoken giant, he is known and respected as "Big Stan" all over the town. Firm but reasonable, he puts a great deal of heart into his safety work. All sensible men concede that some accidents will happen. Big Stan makes this concession from a depth of personal loss that few have experienced. Ten years after he began his devoted service as union safety chairman, his young son came into the plant for summer vacation work. Five weeks later the youth was crushed to death in an elevator accident while on the job.

Big Stan himself does not point a finger of blame. There are theories, but no proof as to how the accident happened. The elevator is an ancient, belt-driven type, given to "creeping" instead of remaining in position at floor level. It can be inadvertently started from one floor just as a man steps into its open door on another floor. The young victim had more youthful zest than mature caution. Nobody knows what happened.

The union had on several occasions complained about the hazard of the elevator, but New York Labor Department and insurance underwriters' inspectors had examined it and pronounced it safe on each occasion. Big, gentle Stan Kasprzak says, "It was just one of those things." He voices no grudges.

In most factories, union safety efforts are more advisory and informal. There seldom is a clearly defined route of enforcement such as that in the Niagara Falls Carborundum plant. When there are immediate decisions to be made, such as whether or not to continue work in an allegedly unsafe situation, members of the more aggressive local union may simply refuse to work without regard to what the labor contract says. As Billy Keller, union safety chairman in the Rock Island refinery at Zionsville, Indiana, puts it, "We'll stop the work to get the job done if we have to." This, at best, is a disorderly approach. It amounts to a wildcat strike by a portion of the employees for any cessation of work contrary to the provisions of the contract is a "wildcat" action. Only a few contracts authorize men to refuse work they deem unsafe.

Quite a few local unions maintain safety committees in their own ranks which have no official status in the eyes of management. Quite a few others have negotiated agreements for joint labor-management committees with equal representation from each side. These joint committees typically are scheduled to meet monthly, but members report many cases in which meetings are not held because managers plead that they are "too busy" on other matters. When meetings are held, union members of the joint committees frequently turn in lists of unsafe conditions they have observed and request corrections. Management takes these suggestions under advisement, then, more often than not, managers fail to take the corrective actions recommended if substantial costs are involved. Too often, unions accept such management attitudes fatalistically.

In plants where there is no joint union-management safety committee, the union may make recommendations and complaints through its standing grievance committee—known in many Oil, Chemical and Atomic Workers locals as the "workmen's committee." The legal powers of such committees on matters of health and safety are vague; they usually act on the basis that they have general rights to express complaints or file formal grievances on any subject pertaining to "working conditions."

Energetic and imaginative union committees can bring considerable pressure on management even in the absence of specific contractual rights. The very filing of a complaint not only poses the issues, but also contributes to building a record in case an accident does occur and any sort of litigation follows. Company officials are mindful of this, thus such letters give managers incentive to correct hazards.

William Higgins, local union president representing Reichhold Chemical Company employees at Elizabeth, New Jersey, is generally complimentary of his management's safety efforts. But he believes in making a record. He says, "We do provide under our grievance procedure that we can write grievances for safety and health and we've had good results. You can file a grievance. If there's no action taken, you can put it in your lawyer's office and it would be on file in case of any real accidents happening through neglect."

Informal but persistent union pressure has brought improvements in many places of work. The National Lead Company plant in Sayreville, New Jersey, has been mentioned in this report several times not because it is necessarily more dangerous than many other places, but because a series of union activities has created an unusually quotable record here.

In the last round of negotiations, the union asked for a safety program which would include the assignment of the union safety chairman to full-time work on health and safety. In view of the fact that nearly 2,000 people work in the plant, 1,200 of them being non-supervisory men belonging to the union, the union thought it reasonable that the company should pay the regular wages of one man selected by the union to perform the non-productive work of checking health and safety from the workers' point of view.

The company declined to bear this expense, but in the course of negotiations made an oral promise to relieve the union safety chairman from his regular work on those occasions when there seemed to be a need for him to engage in safety activities. On a day-to-day basis, the union has responded to this oral concession by asking regularly that the safety chairman be excused from his normal duties to make safety checks. Management has consistently agreed.

Now, John Aquaro, who happens to be a painter, seldom touches a paint brush. Instead, as local union safety chairman, he spends essentially full time touring the facilities, gas mask hanging from his shoulders, investigating conditions and responding to members' complaints. Sometimes at night an employee calls Aquaro at home with a safety problem and the safety chairman returns to the plant to check the situation. Thus the local has effectively secured a full-time safety man with management approval, although the company would not agree formally to his designation.

How much better it would be if all the mickey-mouse arrangements on this vital subject could be replaced by properly negotiated and formalized agreements for union-management sharing of health and safety responsibilities!

No contract can fully outline safe and healthful procedures for a given industrial plant, for the number of potential hazards which may arise is infinite. No union committee can negotiate a health and safety agreement and then walk away presuming the subject covered. Maintenance of proper conditions requires daily surveillance and intermittent corrections.

Labor and management, if there is a willingness on both sides, can negotiate written agreements as to the general conditions which must prevail, the methods by which these general rules may be applied, and the procedures by which differences of opinion between labor and management may be resolved. A written agreement can commit management to provide generally safe and healthful conditions, equipment and operating procedures, all necessary health and safety equipment, including monitoring devices, appropriate in-plant medical facilities and periodic medical examinations, frequent and thorough training of employees on health and safety, and full and clear enunciation of rules and precautions.

A written agreement can commit management to fully inform the union and individual workmen of the chemical nature and the potential health or safety hazards, insofar as they are known, of all substances handled; to inform the union of all conditions recorded by monitoring devices; to inform the individual and, where privacy or medical ethics are not violated, to inform the union of all findings of medical examinations. There can be agreement as to the tightly controlled circumstances under which an individual or a crew may refuse to work. The company can agree to permit health and safety inspections or consultation by outside agencies, public or private, on union request.

Specific application of various written commitments can be worked out in joint labor-management conferences. For example, if the company agrees to provide "adequate" monitoring devices to detect the presence of toxic gases, then company and union can through discussion determine whether one, two, six or whatever number of devices may be appropriate in a given plant, and where they shall be located. And whenever discussions do not result in agreement on such a point, provision can be made for arbitration of the matter before an outside, neutral party.

Records can be kept. These can be valuable not just for the punitive and essentially negative purpose of presenting evidence in lawsuits, but for the positive and humane purpose of saving life or restoring health. If a man goes to a doctor at age 50 with health complaints, that doctor may find diagnosis much more accurate and effective if he is handed a record of the man's previous medical examinations and laboratory tests and also a record of the exposures he has been subject to in the work place. Overall health records and exposure records of an entire work force in a given plant can be of great value to researchers as they attempt to evaluate the long-term effects of particular substances on the human body.

All of these measures can help to move the matter of occupational health and safety out of the present jungle of confusion and mystery and into orderly and responsible surveillance and control.

The managers have not met the responsibility. It is not feasible for them to do so, human nature and economic incentives being what they are. Federal, state and local governments have not done so. Government can and must play a larger role in the future, especially in research and in basic standards setting, yet it will be regrettable if government's police power approach is relied on for most of the basic, day-by-day enforcement activities.

Labor unions stand proudly on the side of the workers, frankly partisan on their behalf. As partisans, they undoubtedly would go to extremes if given the sole responsibility for enactment and enforcement of health and safety standards. But unions, as the representatives of the people who have the most to gain or lose, of the people who sicken and die, have both the right and the obligation to play a leading role.

The challenge to management is to surrender some of its rigidly retained responsibility and control. The challenge to government is to seek out facts and truths about present-day occupational and health hazards and to make its police power available on a standby basis so it can enforce law and order in the workplaces if management and labor fail to do so. The challenge to unions is to fulfill their responsibility to working people by insisting that every man and woman has a safe and healthful place in which to work.

15

How Fare the Neighbors?

Of what concern is industrial health and safety to those people who do not work in industry, but in relatively clean and safe places such as offices, retail stores and college campuses? Aside from ordinary compassion for the general welfare of fellow man, those who do not work in industry have a direct, vested interest. Everyone is the neighbor of industry. Even if one's home or place of work is far from the nearest industrial facility, he may be exposed to the dangers of the thousands of hazardous materials modern industry processes.

Those who work or live near a plant may receive direct and visible "fall out"—escaping dusts, corrosive acids, gases which destroy the paint on houses and surely do the lungs no good. Those who live and work farther away also may suffer unknowingly. There is only a thin envelope of air around the world; pollutants can travel from any one point in this life-giving sheath to any other point. There is but one supply of water; all little brooks run into rivers that run down to the same sea. Many modern chemicals are not biodegradable; that is, they do not decay in reasonable time as natural wastes do. DDT, for example, survives many years, goes all the way to the oceans and upsets the balance of life. When concentrated in the fatty tissues of fish, and the fish are caught, the DDT comes back to haunt us.

Air and water pollution is a much-discussed subject these days. The author elects not to discuss it in detail, to leave it to better qualified observers and analysts. But some observations gleaned from industrial workers, summarized here in only general terms, are pertinent to the growing world-wide concern about general pollution of the environment.

The general public approach is to think of industrial plants as isolated and perhaps as insulated entities. The most enthusiastic proponents of environmental clean-up think in terms of stopping industry from polluting *outside* the plants. They are concerned that air pollutants do not come out of the stacks and over the fences into the neighborhood. They are concerned that waste water be clean when it leaves the company property and flows into the rivers and lakes.

It is not quite that simple. If a deadly gas, vapor or fume is loose inside a plant, at least some of it is going to drift out of the plant. To a lesser extent, solid and liquid materials of offensive nature can go into the general environment if not properly controlled inside the factories. The closer containment of pollutants goes to the original sources—right down to the sub-units of the equipment or right down to the leaking pipe— the better for all concerned, including those who live and work outside.

The author, in his interviews with industrial workers, found nearly all of them intensely concerned with general environmental pollution. Indeed, many of them expressed greater worries about what their plants' emissions were doing to the community as a whole than about exposures within the work place.

The growing public concern about pollution is causing some progress—not enough, but some—to be made toward the elimination of industrial pollution. Worker after worker today makes comments along this general line: "Well, we used to just exhaust so-and-so gas up the stacks but we don't do that anymore because the state has been riding the company's tail about it."

But the offenses continue. Men report being instructed to permit certain emissions, into the air and into sewers, after dark but not during daylight hours. The author has in his files a work order issued in one plant of a very large corporation which instructed employees to slow down certain manufacturing processes during a three-day period when television news cameramen were to tour an adjacent facility. The slow-down was to lessen possibility of leakage of visible pollutants from units making deadly insecticides.

Workers in some plants tell of being ordered to inject perfumes into exhaust gases going up the stacks so that people in the vicinity cannot smell the gases. In one case perfume is used to conceal the distinctive smell of hydrogen sulfide, an injurious gas. In another case where formaldehyde escapes, the people downwind smell roses. But another report, somewhat out of date now, tells of injection of formaldehyde into exhaust gases because this chemical paralyzes the olfactory nerves to the point that the good neighbors cannot smell at all— except for being vaguely aware of a sort of embalming room odor.

Concern about industrial pollution is greatest in the industrial cities such as Cleveland, where occasionally oily scum on the surface of the Cuyahoga River literally catches fire, or Ashtabula, where one night in January, 1970, smog smelling of chlorine rose so thickly from Fields Brook that the policemen went onto a nearby four-lane highway, with gas masks at the ready, to direct traffic.

But pollution affects the countryside, too. An Arkansas farmer complains, "That fog came across the road from the chemical plant; it killed my duck, it killed my pig and it ate the screens off of my windows." A farmer in Missouri had a fine young horse go lame in a pasture two miles from a chemical plant. On the advice of a veterinarian, he moved the horse to another pasture farther away and the horse recovered.

Many industrial plants now are located away from cities, in the green countryside. The countryside becomes less green. Numerous workmen testify that trees in the vicinity of their plants are dying.

Around Pincher Creek, in the foothills of the Canadian Rockies, there is extensive development of natural gas wells containing an extraordinarily high percentage of hydrogen sulfide. Ranchers in the vicinity complain that their bulls are servicing fewer cows, that the pregnant cows are aborting too often, that market-ready cattle weigh a little less than they should. These ranchers cannot prove that hydrogen sulfide is the cause, but they are suspicious.

A farmer who raises barley near Calgary complains that his fence wire and his farm implements are corroding at an accelerated rate since development of natural gas laden with hydrogen sulfide began in that area. He is uneasy for the health of his family, and he has no financial remuneration to offset his worries. In the United States, farmers own the minerals under their soil and sometimes profit quite handsomely when oil or natural gas is found, but in Canada, the surface owner seldom owns mineral rights; these belong to the "Crown" (government) or one of the railroads. Oil companies can come onto the Canadian farmer's land against his wishes, develop the oil and gas, and pay him nothing except compensation for damages done to the few surface acres directly affected. Far north in Canada's sparsely populated bush country and forest land, foliage turns brown and the trees die because of hydrogen sulfide leaks.

Dumping of polluted waste water into rivers and lakes is on the decline, but disposal methods remain far from adequate. Much polluted waste water is pumped into underground wells, where it can seep into the sub-surface aquifers and spread for miles and miles to poison the wells people depend on for domestic water. In one Louisiana plant which handles deadly poisons, wastes are injected into a water table three thousand feet down which is believed to flow out to sea. Who will save the sea?

In one southern industrial plant, water bearing the telltale yellow color of aniline suddenly started boiling out of the ground right in front of the plant office building one day. A hasty excavation project revealed that the water was springing from an old, abandoned oil well, one of many in the vicinity. This plant was injecting wastes into a disposal well and they were spreading underground into old oil wells and coming back to the surface.

The citizen who thinks that industrial poisons are something "over there behind that fence" should be aware that the huge, neatly painted tank truck he follows on the highway or through crowded city streets may be carrying any one of dozens of poisons, acids, or highly explosive fluids or gases. The government is criticized for shipping war gases across country. Industry does it every day, phosgene gas being a common example. Workers tell of spills of toxic materials from trucks onto public streets, where children may step into them en route to school.

A small Texas plant which manufactures sulfuric acid is taken out of operation when a football game is played in a college stadium a few hundred yards away. The rationale seems to be that sudden emission of a large volume of poisonous fumes would cause panic among the 15,000 people who ordinarily fill the stadium when the home team plays. Between ball games, the students are more thinly distributed over the campus and therefore less likely to trample one another in case of panic.

Windsocks on industrial buildings are valuable to the men working there, for they give guidance as to which way to run in case of sudden leakage of large volumes of poisonous gases or fumes. They are not much help to people living or working downwind from the plant.

These examples of unusually callous cases of industrial pollution are listed at random to show the correlation between environment inside the plants and outside. Industry is taking steps to reduce pollution of air and water, but more needs to be done. Not all the corrections can be made from the outside. Pollution control inspectors who sample the air downwind and the water downstream from a factory cannot get the complete facts.

Care needs to be exercised that pollutants are not tossed back and forth across the plant fences, hot-potato fashion. There

are cases in which complaints about conditions inside plants
have caused managers to erect higher exhaust stacks, thus relieving the employees by passing the noxious gases or dusts to
people outside. Conversely, complaints by people outside have
caused some managers to lower stacks, or to re-cycle polluted
waste water, to the detriment of workers inside.

Every reasonable analysis indicates the need for coordination of in-plant and outside-of-plant pollution control efforts.
Controls within the industrial installations obviously benefit
people outside as well as those inside.

Working men and their unions can play a key role in limitation of general pollution, especially by contributing their specialized and specific knowledge of what is going on in the
plants. If workers and their unions are to do this, they must
be brought into partnership by management and by those people
interested in the general environment.

Some environmentalists have failed to recognize this need
for partnership because some of them, to say it plainly, are in-
tellectual snobs. From the heights of more extensive formal
education, some of them look down on men who work with
their hands and sometimes fracture English grammar. They
should bear in mind that the corruption of language will kill
no one, but corruption of air and water will. They should
realize that a pipefitter who knows little or nothing about the
atomic structure of various molecules knows a great deal about
what makes a pipe leak. Those who wish to purify the general
environment must realize that cooperative realism will accomplish more than ivory-towered idealism. Realistic approaches
do not compromise, but instead promote, idealism.

The tremendous pressures of today toward elimination of industrial pollution are posing extreme financial pressure on the
companies. It may be that this is just a matter of chickens coming home to roost, that if industry had been careful and conscientious in past years about avoiding pollution, today's massive
problems would have been avoided. Even if this be so, the
retroactive assignment of blame contributes little or nothing

to future progress. The hard fact of today is that cleaning up the environment, inside the plants and outside, is going to cost industry countless millions of dollars and this cost will be passed on to the consumers. This is the nature of the economic system prevailing in North America—and, for that matter, any economic system anywhere.

The anti-pollution campaign inevitably will lead to the shutdown of some industrial plants. There will be situations in which corporate managers find it economical simply to abandon old facilities and move their operations to newer, better-designed plants. Some environmentalists view such shutdowns with undisguised glee. In this attitude, they are being less than humane. Plant closures inevitably cause serious personal hardships. The industrial worker older than 40, or even older than 35, finds it nearly impossible to secure new employment at equivalent pay. That is the way American industry—and most of American society—works. The objective must be not to shut plants down, but to clean them up, with all deliberate speed but not with bulldozing abandon.

If ever there was a cause which calls for mutual cooperation between every segment of society, it is the cause of eliminating modern poisons and pollutants from our air and water. The rich and the poor, the educated and the uneducated, the manager and the managed, the professional and the working man, all alike can be made ill by pollution. The challenge to all is to participate, but to avoid excluding any other group or individual from the action.

A Closing Commentary

By Frederick A. Linde, P.E.

Chemical engineer and former chemical plants manager

This is an honest book. I can vouch for its honesty: I've worked in very similar plants. The working men quoted did not lie nor distort facts. The gap between factuality and absolute truth is largely, and sincerely, in the mind of the sayer. What the men said, they believed to be factual.

Neither Ray Davidson nor I have any doubt that some of the points were put into the wrong context and sequence. There are exaggerations by men, perhaps—for their having been too close, for years of frustrated inability for betterment, for a lifetime as captives in a system from which release is difficult—but there is no dishonesty.

To really understand what goes on in a process plant, it is necessary to recognize that our chemical plants and oil refineries are very much children of Twentieth Century technology. Nylon was not invented until the mid-thirties. The first sulfuric acid plant using vanadium catalyst in North America was still operating during World War II, and oil refining is a modern industrial miracle.

The skilled crafts are very old: the butcher, the baker and the candlestick maker today use tools and techniques quite the same as those used by their remote counterparts in Pharaonic times. Not so the oil and chemical worker. Where he is no man stood before, and where he is, no one will be again. Complex as they are, these plants change almost daily. The most daring technology of yesterday is common today, obsolete tomorrow.

It is a strange world, where metallurgy and fluid dynamics get more attention than men and where cryogenics are better researched than emphysema. Where the technical literature carries papers on bubble formation in benzene, it is almost completely silent on dermatitis.

Plants are getting bigger, in physical size and production capacity, but usually not in manpower. Equipment is designed to work under extreme conditions. Controlling devices are more reliable, sense more accurately, "feed back" more rapidly, and respond more predictably. The first stainless steel went on the market in about 1922 and now there are literally hundreds of alloys, many custom made for very specialized jobs. Until about 1940, pumps were sealed as they always had been, by squeezing rope around the shaft. They leaked, they needed constant repacking and they limited performance. Then came the mechanical seal and the leakless "canned" pump, and at once a pump could do anything.

Unit production is going up, and so are yields and quality. The larger the plant, the lower the capital cost per unit of production, the lower the unit cost, and the less labor required. Labor use is decreasing, both relatively and absolutely. A 50-ton per day sulfuric acid plant will cost on the order of $500,000, or about $10,000 per daily ton, whereas a 1,000-ton per day plant will cost about $5,000,000, or only $5,000 per daily ton.

The same number of workers can make 50 or 1,000 tons daily—approximately a 2,000 percent decrease in labor costs over the smaller plant. And because the larger plant can afford more controls and recovery apparatus, the yield from it will be significantly better in quantity—from about 95 percent to 99 percent in the case of sulfuric acid.

In petroleum refining, the plants are getting increasingly larger; some now process more than 300,000 barrels of oil a day and do it with fewer people. In 1950, the output for one refinery production worker was 71.2 units; by 1967 it had increased to 191.2 units (based on a 1957-59 index of 100). The average annual increase has been running at a rate of 7.5 percent. (Source: U. S. Department of Labor Bulletin 1652, December, 1969.) At the present rate at which refinery labor productivity is increasing, in mid-1976 only one-half as many men will be used to refine the same quantity as were used in 1967.

It takes years to put a new "grass roots" process plant into initial operation. Economic surveys, basic research, pilot plant studies, market evaluation, site selection, engineering design, equipment specifications and purchase all precede the actual plant construction. Entire catalogs of design and purchase specifications are prepared. Precise construction schedules, flow diagrams and computerized data processing guide the delivery, issue and placement of each nut and bolt.

Is labor cataloged? No! What about health hazards? Not in the catalog. Precise design of the shipping drums will be specified, but nothing is said about the man to fill the drum, or what the material in the drum will do to him.

What of the men who work in an industry where manpower seems almost incidental, almost an afterthought, in all planning and preparations?

It is not a bright outlook. Fifty years ago the most typical worker could aspire to promotion and dignity, providing only that he gave the boss some loyalty, used some skill and intelligence and got a few breaks. On that simple formula he could become a foreman, then a superintendent, perhaps a manager, maybe even have his own factory and be his own boss. There was a time when guts, vision, hard work and good luck were the essentials for starting in business. In 1901, Monsanto was started with a capital of $6,000, and now it is America's third largest chemical company. Rare is the man so stupid or so optimistic, particularly if he has worked in a plant, to try that in 1970.

Today a worker may hope for a foremanship, but that, too, is a dismal life. As a foreman he surrenders all support from organized labor and gains none from the corporation. He is subject to all kinds of dreadful indignities, shift changes, transfers, overtime work without pay and the duty to carry out a policy about which he was not consulted, cannot modify and frequently distrusts.

The heavy thinkers in industry decided, some years ago, that raw engineers were just the thing for supervision. (This probably accounts for some of the lamentations over declining engineering school enrollments—and for the decline.) The conventional wisdom went something like this: the engineer is already trained and it won't cost much to "mold" him into our way of doing things; he is eager and ambitious and will work long, hard hours and won't ask for overtime; he can be watched and the best (i.e., most adaptable) can be promoted; and he won't have any nonsense about unions and he won't be too concerned with people. Now, this policy is even being extended to foremen.

Under such circumstances, the typical worker sees little to brighten the prospect. Some jobs are dull and repetitious. Some jobs require skilled hands and practical know-how, but supervision, increasingly in the hands of college-trained technicians who have not worked with their hands, belittles these skills. Some jobs require tremendous responsibility for controlling equipment which produce fantastic volumes of profitable materials, but suggestions emanating from the more imaginative of these men get less and less recognition from above. No longer is the typical work force a continuum of ascending experience and responsibility from newest laborer to plant manager; instead the worker, even the most skilled and responsible worker, is isolated from the management which controls him.

The process plant worker frequently is not told just what he is working with and frequently he does not see the product he makes—the product may be just noises in tubes and marks on charts so far as his personal identification with it is concerned. The process operator cannot market his know-how to another employer, as allegedly is the opportunity of the free enterprise system, for his training is too specialized to be of value in another plant and modern economics mitigate against the hiring of older, experienced people when healthier young men are available.

Add to these frustrations the messiness, discomforts and indignities of many work environments, and the unknown dangers of working with an ever-changing mix of new materials.

Young men coming into industry often work a few days, then walk away from the smells, the noise, the stinging burns of acids and other materials. Young wives often urge their husbands to do this, especially when the men come home with strange chemical odors on their breaths and when colored stains seep out of their pores after repeated baths. Turnover among young workers is quite heavy in chemical plants.

When the worker reaches what should be the prime of life, at perhaps age 40, he realizes that he is locked in. He acknowledges the limitations of his life, the fact that he can no longer get a decent job in the open market, and he knows that he will not be a whole man until retirement. He works and waits for the last day in the plant. It becomes his Holy Grail, the one sure rock to which to cling.

He observes his older fellow workers, their decreasing vitality, their respiratory ills, their heart seizures and high blood pressures and burn scars. Suppose he retires and has a heart attack? Or an ulcer? Or cancer? In one fateful moment a life is wasted. Cost of medical treatment aside, retirement won't be as it was planned. Was it wise to follow this job, to be sick, to touch the Grail and have it slip away?

Thus the fanatic concern among industrial workers for health and safety, for ever earlier retirement, for hospital and medical insurance while at work and after retirement.

Relatively few people ever see the inside of a chemical plant or an oil refinery. People drive past them and are awed by their size and impressed by the lights at night. (For some reason, brilliantly lighted plants are much in vogue.) They see sanitized glimpses in TV commercials and they think it is a sleek miracle-world closed to mere mortals.

In fact, the plants embody all of the frailties of humanity.

They are frequently so ill-designed and badly built that they must be shut down and re-done before they will operate at a profit. The tip-off is the terse, short paragraph in the annual report, in the section explaining why earnings fell below anticipated levels, that "start-up expenses in the East Overshoe plant exceeded expectations."

Much that goes into a plant is improvisation. Even though the range of metal alloys is very large, some substances cannot be economically contained in any metal. Then glass, ceramics and various plastics are substituted. All of these have their own limitations of temperature, age, vibration, stress or impact. A conscientious engineer tries to determine corrosion before selecting a material of construction, but no laboratory is a substitute for actual experience. Thus, the plant frequently becomes the corrosion lab, and piping gets put in and replaced at frequent intervals.

Sometimes a choice is poorly made and then it's a disaster. Although a lot of effort goes into this end of the business, the leaks which occur fall on the innocent as well as the not so innocent. Until progress ends and technology gets frozen, there will be leaks, ruptures and other malfunctions, but they can be minimized. Many, many of the hazards described in this book can be eliminated.

Joints and connections can be placed so that if they leak, they do so in untraveled areas. More attention can be paid to mounting and suspensions. More expansion joints can be used. Process piping invariably is grouped together and carried on overhead racks; instead, vulnerable pipe runs can be put in trenches.

Certain types of shields are practical. Pipe and vessel thickness can be accurately measured in a variety of ways and when potential weaknesses show up, replacement—whether convenient or not—can be made.

Stacks and vents are offensive. They get rid of fumes from the immediate area, but only to pollute the air in some other part of the plant, or beyond the plant fence. Much vent-ing and stacking is unnecessary, for fumes can be absorbed, mists collected by precipitators and dusts filtered. When such techniques are necessary for profitable operation, they now are used. A phosphorous burner, producing phosphoric acid, would be totally uneconomical without an electrostatic precipitator. It can be used to keep the air clean, as well as to make money.

Process plants usually are characterized by a lot of steam rising in various places. It might be pure steam, or it might be exhaust from a jet and be contaminated, but it is vented into the atmosphere simply because it is cheaper to do this than to condense it and return the condensate to the boilers. While picturesque, steam can be a distinct hazard, especially in cold weather, and more than one worker has lost his way in a steam cloud.

Polluted water can be cleaned. It is done in Germany in central treatment units; there are specialized plants designed specifically for multi-plant industrial waste waters. In spite of all the self-righteous talk by industry, most plant effluent is dumped into our rivers, lakes and seas without any attempt at cleaning. Simply dumped.

There are many toxicity monitoring and detecting devices on the market. They can "sniff out" such deadly substances as cyanide, hydrogen sulfide, carbon monoxide, chlorine and hydrocarbons and detect changes in air composition. Although only modestly expensive, they frequently are hard to maintain. Maintenance costs money. Besides, the mere presence of such devices is pretty tangible evidence that the area bears watching. This might give the men bad ideas!

Leaks around agitator shafts and from kettles usually can be contained. Even though he can't buy it from a manufacturer, an imaginative engineer can design and build a seal from simple components.

Noise! It is one of the worst industrial indignities and it is becoming recognized for its harm to health as well as hearing. Plants are becoming noisier; even shouts can't be heard in high pressure steam plants and compressor stations. Much packing equipment uses compressed air and the constant clanging of metal and hissing of exhaust air is nerve-wracking.

At our present level of knowledge, it is not possible to design a silent plant, but we do have more than enough knowledge to "knock off" the peak of noise, to reduce its level from maybe 100 decibels to 75 decibels. Major noise makers can be isolated; noise can be deflected by louvres or absorbed (noise is energy and obeys the usual laws which govern energy).

Efficient air intake and exhaust mufflers can be bought or built. The annoying, deep-pitched rumble of machinery, if anticipated during design, can be cut down with cushioning. A lot of noise is simply poor or lazy design, or testimony to the fact that the design engineer never worked in a plant. More and better steam traps and skillful replacement of condensate drains will prevent the water hammer in a steam pipe which can scare the bejabbers out of the most hardened operator.

Some process plant hazards are inevitable, but more skill and thought will stop many. Some can be prevented at little or no cost simply by the application of some concern for health, some foresight. Others will cost money—not really very much money—in capital costs for better original equipment and in maintenance costs. Many foreign companies spend this money.

In recent years, consumers have become aware that a number of chemicals and drugs in which they had placed faith were in fact dangerous to health. By force of law, some of these have been taken off the market. What of the men who manufactured these products? These men most often handle the products in highly concentrated form, or they handle intermediate components of the unhealthful products in stages where they are substantially more toxic. The banning of certain chemicals, drugs, food additives and insecticides from the market has come about because testing, subsequent to the products being put on the market, has revealed *new* information about the dangers. Should not there be more pre-testing before a substance is placed on the market, or handled in more than laboratory or pilot plant scope operations by workmen?

Costs are involved—costs in original research and capital investment in equipment, costs in delayed production, costs in more scrupulous management—in many of these precautionary efforts. But these costs seem reasonable, and certainly proper, for the protection of our greatest resource—people. The people who work in industry can be, and should be, protected against undue hazards to life and health.